The Life That Gave Birth
To The Animals

George Pearson

Published by snagaP Publishing

Sex, Brown Ale and Rhythm & Blues

Written by George Pearson

Cover Design by George Pearson & Tony Metcalfe
from an idea by David Park

Designed by Tony Metcalfe

Scanning by Chris Willis

Newcastle Skyline illustration by Kev Stevens

Photographs by Stan Atkinson, Alex Baird, Eric Burdon
and George Pearson

Printed by CP Offset Limited
Kellaw Road, Yarm Road Industrial Estate,
Darlington, Co. Durham.

ISBN 0 9534664 0 X

Printed & bound in the United Kingdom
on 100gm matt art by George Pearson

Typeset in Novarese Book

Acknowledgements

Sincere thanks to my wife Elaine and daughters Lucy and Sadie, for their help and support and for guiding me through the mysteries of information technology.

Thank you to Animals drummer Johnny Steel for giving me access to his diaries and to Ann Steel for editing my efforts, though any errors are my own. Both Johnny and Ann bolstered me with enthusiastic encouragement.

I am grateful for the co-operation of two other members of The Animals, guitarist Hilton Valentine and the late Chas Chandler. Thanks also to Alan Carr, Danny Okpoti, Dave Wilson, Stan Atkinson and Alex and Jean Baird for their help and information.

There are many others who have assisted in the production of this book, though unnamed they are not forgotten.

Introduction

To be young and interested in music and style in the late 50's in Britain was an exercise in frustration. In the early part of the decade post war youth had enjoyed its first flush of rebellion and self-expression. "Teddy Boys" did not have their mode of dress dictated to them by the fashion moguls of the day. The many and varied styles were invented by the kids themselves and made- to- measure by horrified bespoke tailors to whom 4 button drapes in canary yellow with purple velvet collars were anathema.

The music too was wild and undisciplined. Elvis Presley pumped out raw black blues music, Jerry Lee Lewis played the piano with his feet and Buddy Holly pioneered a quieter but no less unique musical style. On the home front, skiffle swept the country and thousands of kids in hundreds of church halls were making their own music. By 1959, Buddy Holly was dead, Elvis was in the army and big business was back in charge, inflicting the Italian style of short box jackets and winkle-picker shoes on an apathetic public.

However in Newcastle upon Tyne a multi-faceted but like minded group of young people were ignoring what was being foisted on them by the music and fashion industry and finding their own way. The books of Steinbeck, Salinger, Kerouac and Sillitoe, the poetry of Ginsberg, Ferlinghetti, the films of Elia Kazan and black American blues from Leadbelly to Joe Turner were influencing them. At the same time, they were also absorbing their own folk music, which was enjoying a renaissance due to the earlier influence of skiffle.

On the question of style, raggedness and self-expression were all. Clothing must be customised and well-worn, Army and Navy stores were the main source of supply. Anything that would horrify, shock, disgust or generally irritate the more conventional members of Society was to be pursued. If a spontaneous eruption of a change in the style and direction of a whole section of the youth of today were to take place it would be pored over by pundits and academics, branded as a movement and recorded as being of great significance. However, this storm in the sea of conformity went largely unrecorded.

Invariably youth finds self-expression in music and any group of young people contains some aspiring musicians. This gang of rebels was no exception. Experimenting with music as uncompromising as their style in clothing and manners, these kids were definitely outside the mainstream of popular music. If the puerile lyrics of Cliff Richard's "Living Doll" or the asinine dance steps of the Shadows were a recipe for success they didn't want to know about it. They were too busy cooking up their own pie and if people didn't like the taste, too bad! But "The Times They Were a-Changing" as Bob Dylan was later to recount. By the summer of 1964, five young Geordies made musical history, topping the American charts with a single that was four and a half minutes long. The Animals had made it. This is the story of where they came from, what influenced them, and the people they met along the way.

The Hole
in the Wall Gang

Eric Victor Burdon swayed precariously and tightened his grip on the branch he was holding; his cowboy booted feet maintaining an uncertain balance on a jagged boulder. Eric had just administered the final flourish of a piece of graffiti, or artistic self-expression, depending on your point of view. Daubed on the weathered brown stone of this long abandoned quarry face, in red lead paint in letters two feet high, were the words "The Pagans". Judging from the rather blurred quality of the letters "THE PAG" and the large quantities of dry red paint staining the artist's clothing and flesh, together with the many empty Newcastle Brown Ale bottles littering the ground, it was safe to assume that the bulk of this work had been undertaken when the perpetrator was the worse for drink. The artist's canvas was part of the end wall of a box canyon hewn out of the rock by quarry workers of the distant past. Long ago reclaimed by nature, the walls were overgrown with lichen, and a variety of hardy plants and grasses maintained a precarious existence on the weathered stone. The entrance to this natural hideaway was screened by shrubs and young saplings, making it a perfect spot for anyone not wishing to be noticed by the public at large.

Such were the present residents of this lonely spot. Not that they had done anything wrong, but they preferred to site themselves where no passing policeman, gamekeeper or plain old busybody was liable to ask them any boring questions. In addition to Eric, 11 other people inhabited this latter day hoboes' jungle on this cold October Sunday morning, all in various states of wakefulness.

Eric administered a final flourish and leapt from his perch, turning to face what he fondly imagined to be his audience. The remains of last night's fire still smouldered in the centre of the clearing, and the burly figure of Big Alex Baird crouched over it, absorbed in taking the chill out of a half empty bottle of brown ale overlooked in the flickering shadows of the previous evening. Wearing black jeans and wellington boots turned down like seaman's boots, he had a piratical air about him; indeed, he was given to performing impressions of Robert Newton's Long John Silver, usually on pub tables. This invariably resulted in him being ejected from the establishment, especially as he usually insisted on having someone perched on his shoulder to play the parrot.

Next to Alex was Crockett. Thanks to Fez Parker's portrayal of the American folk hero Davy Crockett in Walt Disney's sanitised version of his life, any young man in the late fifties named David was almost bound to be nicknamed Davy Crockett. This particular Davy had more in common with one of the other heroes of the Alamo, Jim Bowie, given his fascination with knives, and particularly as at that moment Crockett was brandishing a 14" blue steel bayonet. He was using the bayonet to chop up a faded wooden notice bearing the legend "Dangerous. Keep out. High Explosives." In Crockett's expert hands the razor sharp blade sliced through the old wood, producing long slivers suitable for re-igniting the dying fire.

Watching the proceedings with great interest was one whose only desire at that moment was to be warm. Alan Price was a civil servant by necessity and a piano player by inclination. His attire, dark white mac, black trousers and pointed shoes, topped off by button down collar and dark tie, was suitable for a civil servant and/or a modern Jazz fan, but not ideal for sleeping outdoors in October without a tent. Pricey thrust his hands deeper into his pockets and shivered. Last night he was playing a piano in Gateshead, this morning he was somewhere in Northumberland wearing a perplexed expression.

Propped up against the cliff wall, in a place with a protective overhang, were three powerful motor bikes: a Norton Featherbed, a Triumph Bonneville and a B.S.A. Goldstar. Together they represented the most powerful bikes available from the three main British manufacturers in what was the heyday of British motor cycles. The Norton belonged to Crockett and the Triumph and B.S.A. were owned by two brothers, Joe and Jimmy Chambers. Joe was blonde, long, lean and rangy, and looked as if he'd be more at home on a cow pony rather than a motorbike. An engineer by trade and lover of all things mechanical, he was lovingly employed with spanners and feeler gauges, making sure his machine was in perfect running order.

Meanwhile, Jimmy, having located a tiny natural spring trickling from the mossy mouth of a fissure in the rock, was occupied washing his own chiselled features and combing his swept back, short black hair. Although Jimmy wore the black leather boots and jacket of a biker, he could only be described as dapper. Jimmy's sole purpose in life was to meet, pursue and screw members of the fair sex, to this end he always kept himself neat and tidy.

They had chosen to build their fire near an old tree that had died and tumbled over years before and was now the home of a great many varieties of fungi and millions of wood boring insects. Perched on this ancient seat was Hank, a black clad figure with long hair and sideburns of the same colour, his white teeth contrasting sharply with his blue jowls. At his feet lay his dog, Willy, a huge creature resembling a heavily maned wolf, with coarse, red, fox coloured hair. Willy's looks were as fierce as his nature was gentle, rather like his hairy master. After hawking and spitting noisily, Hank spoke, "Is that the name of your old band then, Eric?" Without appearing to be interested in obtaining a reply. Eric, looking pleased to have elicited some kind of a response to his efforts, slung the paintbrush into the undergrowth and replied, "Aye, we used to use that name but it sounds a bit like a trad band these days. Ah think it would be a good way of describing you lot, you're a load of Pagans."

"If you mean worshippers of idols and eaters of raw flesh," said Big Alex, now drinking the defrosted brown ale with some relish, "I must admit I'm mad on Louis Armstrong, and that pork pie I had last night wasn't very well cooked.." Eric ignored this quip and continued to address the company, "What we're playing is Rhythm 'n Blues, what we need is an American bluesy sort of name." "We are The Squatters," boomed a deep voice from near the roots of Hank's dead tree. The voice emanated from a huge unkempt figure engaged in disentangling himself from his tattered sleeping bag. This was Jackie Hogg, better known as Animal. 6' 2" of hairy, wild raggedness, Animal hauled himself to his feet by the tree roots, emerging from his night quarters still fully clothed in combat jacket, thick cord trousers and still wearing welly boots turned down like Alex's. If this band of reprobates had been called upon to elect a leader, it would have been Animal Hogg. He was certainly the most respected, revered and notorious of the bunch. A slight frisson of fear passed over Eric's eyes at this interruption, and he turned his gaze towards Animal with some apprehension. "Anyway, the only squatting Ahm ganna dee at the moment is hev a good shite." So saying, Jackie strode off through the undergrowth to fulfil his mission.

The noise disturbed another figure lying in the matted dead grass near Animal's chosen headquarters. Red haired, red bearded and known only as Red, he was a man of few words, none of which he felt inclined to utter now. Clad in a ragged tweed overcoat with deep patch pockets and clutching a huge staff fashioned from a single beech sapling, he clumped over to the tree stump and sat down next to Hank. His hair was similar in colour to the dog Willy, who now bellied over for a stroke.

Most of the figures in this misty morning scene blended in pretty well with the muted browns and greens of the autumnal surroundings, but against the rock wall, near the motorbikes, was a palette of colours standing out clearly against the brown background. Sitting on their folded sleeping bags, with their backs against the rock face, sat two girls. Jean Reay, tall with short blonde hair, was wearing a bright blue combat style jacket and mustard coloured jeans. Little Paula, with dark, wavy, shoulder length hair, was enveloped in a bright red duffle coat with tight maroon cords, Both wore proper cleated brown hiking boots with heavy white socks turned over them. The boots and socks somehow contrived to be comparatively clean in these grubby surroundings. Their choice of bright clothing was deliberate - as their main means of moving around the country was hitch-hiking, they believed in being highly visible. Enjoying the first cigarette of the day, the two sat as if watching a play, acted out by a not very talented group of children. Their scrubbed, make up free faces wore an expression of amused tolerance. Jean and Paula were also waiting for the fire to blaze up, then die down to a stage suitable for cooking on. Unlike most of the boys they were less inclined to live on a diet of beer and pork pies, and their rucksacks contained all the ingredients necessary for a decent breakfast.

Only one person had not been disturbed by the general hubbub. Nestling on a piece of soft grass between two lichen encrusted slabs of sandstone to the right of Eric's rocky canvas, lay a blonde youth in a decent waterproof sleeping bag, snoring gently. Johnny Steel was always the drummer in whichever band Burdon and Pricey were currently forming, disbanding or practising with at any given point in time. Johnny did not often go away for weekends in the country and was usually attired in elegant clothing suitable for the clubs and pubs of the city. On his occasional forays into the backwoods, he tended to borrow his dad's windcheater. His dad was a fishmonger and made his way down to the Shields quay at 4 o'clock every morning, wearing his windcheater, to buy his fish fresh. So the front of the coat was encrusted with fish scales, consequently Johnny's sleeping form exuded the distinct smell of fish.

Crockett's fire making efforts had finally borne fruit, and the fire began to crackle and blaze. Alex piled on more dry branches and the flames grew higher. Suddenly Willy stood up and growled although his tail still wagged. Two figures were crashing through the saplings, bushes and brambles masking the entrance to the hideout, kicking their way through the golden carpet of autumn leaves and laughing joyously. Leading the way through the tangled undergrowth was Geronimo. Black, greased-back hair, dark brooding eyes and swarthy good looks, together with a black, fringed jacket, skin tight jeans and a six inch hunting knife strapped to his waist, made the nickname almost inevitable. Just behind came Terry Molloy, his red plaid lumber jacket showing bright through the trees, cowboy boots crunching the leaves. Terry's short combed-forward red hair and freckled face reminded people of a cartoon character called Sunblest Sammy, currently extolling the delights of Sunblest bread. This had resulted in Terry being given the sobriquet of Sunblest.

Although Geronimo looked sullen, he was in fact a humorous lad, and not above sending himself up. "Geronimo has um liberated

Some of the Squatters -
Eric Burdon far left.

much milk from um white man's doorsteps," he shouted, adopting his Little Plum Indian's voice and producing bottles of milk from under his leather jacket. "Also liberated many eggs from um white man's hens laying away from home," chorused Sunblest. The winter sun was low in the sky and suddenly the clouds parted and a shaft of sunlight slanted its way through the trees behind Geronimo and Sunblest, casting their shadows towards, and illuminating, the scene before them. Geronimo ploughed on, but Terry stopped, the better to drink in and appreciate what he saw. Grouped in this wild place, encapsulated in the warming sun's beam, these young people could almost have been some ancient tribe of forest people, so elemental were they. Poised in time. City dwellers every one, and yet they seemed totally at one with their surroundings, as if this was their natural inheritance, and not the noisy, hectic turmoil that passed for normality in the Twentieth Century. Terry stood gaping, wondering how he had ever got to know these people and so glad to be accepted by them and part of them, that for a moment "the smoke from the fire got into his eyes."

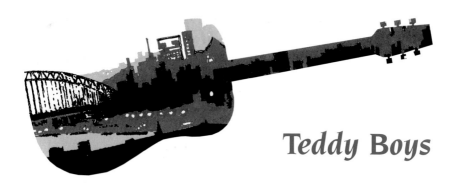

Teddy Boys

Terry Molloy was a war baby born in 1940, a teenager in 1953 when the very word had just come into common usage. At 15 Terry left school, donned his boiler suit, bought the Daily Mirror and ten Woodbines, and set off for the factory. From childhood to manhood overnight. A week of coughing soon made him decide that he would have to be a man without the use of cigarettes, but he stuck with the Mirror. Brought up in a mining village, Terry had always known that he would never go down the pit, having seen the terrible lung diseases, broken limbs and blue scars suffered stoically by the fathers of his school friends: he knew there had to be another life. He and one other boy in his class took jobs in the nearest town, Newcastle; the rest went into mining as a matter of course.

To be a young man in 1955, and to aspire towards even a semblance of style, was to be a Teddy boy, and Terry was soon at the Co-op tailors in Cramlington being measured for his first Ted suit. Some weeks later, attired in a silver grey drape jacket with roll collar, 16" drainpipe trousers and blue, crepe soled, wedge heeled shoes, Terry set off with his best mate, Davy Tunnah heading for the 'Bottom House' in Burradon for his first taste of beer

Davey pushed open the brass handled door, with etched glass panels showing the name of the pub, and they stepped into the spartan environs of the public bar. Davey had already been drinking for some months, and made his way confidently to the horseshoe shaped bar which dominated the room. Terry followed behind him, his heart beating wildly, trying to look self-assured. In a mining village if you were old enough to work, you were old enough to drink, and their expensive suits bore witness to the fact they were earning money. The landlord served them without comment and they carried the brimming glasses of ale over to the table football machine. Four young Teds were already hunched over it, earnestly belting the ball back and forth; Davy placed his sixpence on the corner of the table to play the winners. Not surprisingly, Terry found he didn't like the taste of beer much, but drank it manfully, and the second glass did not seem so bad. It was Saturday night and their ultimate destination was the Burradon dance. Terry was relieved when Davey decided it was time to go, he had managed three pints and could feel the beer swilling around in his stomach.

The dance was at the other end of the village, almost a mile away, and they set off walking, crepe soles splashing through the puddles, hands in pockets, drape jackets flying in the breeze. Davey broke into song and Terry joined in, soon the words and harmonies of Unchained Melody echoed round the damp streets. Terry was overcome by feelings of boozy euphoria, he sang louder.

Although Teddy boys have always been synonymous with early rock and roll, the style came before the music. In London in 1953 a bunch of young toffs were experimenting with wearing 'Edwardian' style clothing. The fashion was soon taken over by working class kids and bastardised out of all recognition. By 1954, the expression Teddy boy was common parlance and a breakdown in youthful morals was confidently forecast. At that time only two rock & roll records made the British top twenty. Sh-Boom by the Crew Cuts made no. 4 in October '54 and Bill Haley and the Comets occupied the no.8 spot in the same month. In 1954, Bill Haley's "Rock around the Clock" was in the Top Twenty and would be no. 1 by Christmas, but these two degenerate youths, inflamed by drink preferred ballads.

As they approached the village hall the boys could hear the

trumpet player of the band murdering "Oh Mein Papa", a major instrumental hit the year before, by Eddie Calvert. Suddenly Terry began to feel dizzy, and just as quickly was violently sick into the shrubbery surrounding the building. Davey stood with his arm around his shoulders mumbling the usual platitudes on the lines of, "bring it up, you'll feel better for it." Terry soon recovered and, wiping his mouth with his handkerchief, did feel better. The pair had soon paid over their shillings and joined the rest of the youths clustered at the opposite end to the band. They watched the dancers, mostly girls, as the pubs had not yet disgorged enough young men with the confidence to make the transition from spectator to participant

During the next weeks and months Terry visited many more pubs and dances in this and the surrounding villages, becoming as self - assured and swaggering a young Turk as any of the rest of this post-war generation of youth, with "more money than sense". The object of Saturday night for some of the expensively clad tearaways was to rip the elegant clothes off the backs of one of their fellows, usually someone from another village. At some point in the evening there would be a spontaneous eruption of violence, sparked by some minor incident. Soon the hall would be a mass of writhing, multi-coloured bodies, fists and crepe soled shoes whacking into chins and shins, bloody noses staining the dance floors. Most of this mayhem was of a ritual nature and the stitching up that needed to be done was usually securing sleeves and lapels back onto jackets rather than the suture type. Publicans, invisible menders and dry cleaners were the main beneficiaries of Saturday nights. Terry usually avoided becoming involved in these celebrations of manhood unless his mates were being picked on, then tribal instincts took over, the adrenaline flowed and he pitched in with the rest, trying his best not to incur any costly tailoring bills.

According to the popular press of today, the female equivalent of Teddy boys were black angels, girls who dressed entirely in black and wore white make-up. If this was so, the girls in the pit villages of Northumberland did not subscribe to the fashion. They wore big frocks with petticoats and white high heels, the more daring ones tight skirts with very tight sweaters after the movie stars of the day. Rather than fight, Terry attempted to learn to dance and chatted up the girls with a view to taking them home and trying to get his hand up the big frocks or loosen the bras under the tight sweaters. Walking a girl home could often involve a long walk if they lived in another village, 3 miles or more was not uncommon. It often occurred to Terry that he could never get a girl to stop for a necking session in the middle of one of these long treks, yet they seemed quite happy to have a half hour grapple at their own front door. It did not occur to him that most girls were wise to the ways of boys. They knew that, to use a common expression of the day, "a standing prick has no conscience," and if you were going to get a boy excited, it was better to be within shouting distance of your mam and dad. On these occasions, if he was lucky he might be able to slide his hands up the skirt of the big frock, past the suspenders, pull aside the cotton lined gusset and slip his finger into that lubricious hood of delights, that was the goal of all men young and old. There were many coarse descriptions for this activity, later to be immortalised in song by The Beatles in "Penny Lane" as "fish and finger pie". Suffice to say that, if a boy should be so fortunate, he could walk home with his hands thrust deep in his overcoat pocket, conserving that delicate aroma, to sustain him through his masturbatory fantasies.

Serving a six-year apprenticeship as a printer in Newcastle opened Terry up to a lot more influences than were to be found in a closed mining community. One of the many apprentices he worked with was a lean, lanky eighteen-year-old named Don Ritzema. Don spent most of his free time when his machine was running blowing a trumpet mouthpiece - to keep his chops in shape, as he put it. Don aspired to play trumpet in a jazz band, devoting most of his spare time to achieving this end. The two got on very well at work and Terry was flattered when Don asked him if he would like to accompany him to the Newcastle Jazz Club, a Tuesday night club held in the Celebration Hall at the Royal Arcade. The club was situated on the second floor, directly above the headquarters of the Newcastle Cycling Club. Two active members of this club, who were also ardent jazz fans, were Chas Chandler and Alex Baird. The pair had attended Heaton High School together, where they became members of the school band, simply for the opportunity to learn an instrument. Both were destined to be influential in Terry's life throughout his teenage years.

The jazz club was founded and officiated over by Alan Brown who loved the music with a passion and was intent on spreading the gospel to anyone who would listen. In addition to booking a broad selection of bands, Alan had an extensive jazz library and any member of the club was welcome to borrow the books free of charge. Terry was soon taking books home, filling his mind with information about everyone from Buddy Bolden to Charlie Parker.

One of the most popular bands was The Panama Jazzmen, led by trumpeter Joe McMullen, and Terry was impressed to find that Don knew them well. This meant that he was able to listen in on the stories, jokes and musical anecdotes that were the stock in trade of musicians everywhere. The club had no drinks licence, but Alan would allow the musicians to bring in drink and it soon fell on Terry to go next door to the Engineers club for the bottles. His best customer was trombonist Ronnie Maclean, wit, raconteur and brown ale drinker extraordinaire. In later years, Ronnie was to play in the Newcastle Big Band alongside bass player Gordon Sumner, who habitually wore a brown and yellow striped sweater. Ronnie gave him the nickname "Sting", so contributing to rock and roll history.

What fascinated Terry most, apart from the music, were the people who attended. There was a broad cross section of types, ages and modes of dress. Also, Terry was later to discover, many different professions and social classes. They all had two things in common, their love of the music and their ability to jive. Jiving was the cream in the coffee of jazz, an extemporaneous means of self-expression matching the improvisation of the music. The dance was first seen in Britain during the war, when thousands of American GIs were stationed in Britain and invaded the dance halls, clubs and pubs, leaving an indelible stamp on the British way of life before joining our forces to invade Europe. First established in London, jiving soon spread to the provinces and found its main expression in the jazz clubs, every city evolving its own style. The Newcastle Jazz club was particularly fortunate in being visited regularly by most of the black crew members of an American merchant ship called the Bermuda Star, which docked on the Tyne every six months, and their frenetic dancing style greatly influenced the locals.

Given Terry's preoccupation with the opposite sex, the female members of the club were a revelation. They were definitely not of the big frock variety he was comfortable with. These girls had a degree of poise and sophistication as well as an ability to dance that left Terry totally in awe. He could not imagine ever being able to talk to or dance with these exotic creatures. However, nipping out at interval times with Don and his friends for a friendly libation in the Duke of Wellington or the Monkey Bar soon broke down his reserve. He was soon chatting to the girls and found that they did not despise him for not being able to dance, indeed they were quite happy to show him how, their own skill and timing making him appear more proficient than he really was. In a few weeks he was bopping away with the best of them, and, as he invariably hung on until the last minute and had to run for the last bus home, found Tuesday nights exhilarating. but exhausting.

This was the start of a love affair with Jazz and Terry began to attend the regular jazz concerts held at the Newcastle City Hall. One of the many bands he saw at that time was led by a man whose unintentional role in creating the future shape of British popular music has been largely ignored. Trumpeter and bandleader Ken Colyer was a purist, and insisted on playing only New Orleans jazz. He also took an interest in American Blues and folk music. Just to break up his set he introduced a feature where he played guitar, accompanied by the bass and banjo player, and sang songs by people such as Woody Guthrie. Colyer's insistence on playing only pure New Orleans jazz led to friction, and eventually mutiny. The whole band walked out on him, and a new band was formed under the aegis of trombonist Chris Barber, with Pat Halcox taking the trumpet chair. The ever-astute Chris Barber retained the popular "skiffle" sessions, as they came to be known, and banjo player Lonnie Donegan switched to guitar and took over the singing role. These sessions became so popular that Donegan realised he had stumbled onto something with huge potential, and it was not long before he left Barber and formed his own skiffle group. January 1956 saw him at no. 8 in the top twenty with Rock Island Line, and a string of other hits followed. Here at last was music the kids could play themselves, and the sales of guitars rocketed. Those who couldn't afford a guitar settled for washboard or tea chest bass. Many of the bands that were to come into prominence in the 60's, including The Beatles, cut their musical teeth on skiffle. Ken Colyer continued his career in Jazz, but his life was dogged by illness, and he was found dead in a beach chalet in the South of France in 1990. He died alone and penniless, his contribution to the cultural life of Britain almost forgotten.

Don soon introduced Terry to the other jazz venue in town, "The New Orleans Jazz Club", which ran on Friday, Saturday and Sunday nights. Although there was no dance floor, it did have a bar, a very important consideration for two young men hell bent on living the decadent life they associated with the music. The club was situated on Melbourne Street in a run-down area of the district of Shieldfield. Soon to be ripped apart in a frenzy of urban renewal, it was a place of gas lamps, cobbled streets and iron balconies redolent of Tenessee Williams' portrayal of New Orleans in the film "A Street Car Named Desire". The resident band on Saturday nights was The Vieux Carre Jazzmen whose musical policy was very much on the lines of Ken Colyer's. They also included a folk and blues spot featuring banjo player Pete Deucher, a huge, black bearded bohemian figure, heir to the Deucher brewery fortune, who had been disowned by his family for playing jazz. Deucher's choice of material would never be recorded, nor even be suitable for a concert stage in those puritanical times, as he seemed to go to great lengths to ferret out the filthiest blues lyrics possible. Here is a typical example:

What's that smells like fish momma?

Daddy wants to know
What's that smells like fish momma?
Daddy wants to know.
You come down the road
Swearing like hell
I can tell what you've bin doing
By the way you smell.
What's that smell like fish momma?
Daddy wants to know.

Terry was destined to mis-spend a good deal of his youth in the smoky, boozy arms of this whore of Shieldfield, and he loved every minute of it.

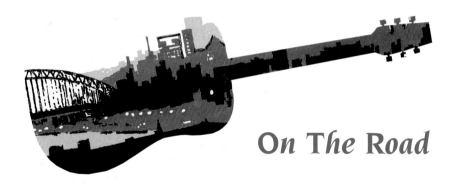

On The Road

1956 proved to be a seminal year for rock and roll. Bill Haley was already well established, skiffle was sweeping the country and in May, Elvis Presley appeared at no. 13 in the top twenty. This pouting, sneering, gyrating young man, oozing sex appeal and menace, created a sensation on both sides of the Atlantic and spawned a thousand imitators. Elvis's success seemed to open the floodgates and this exciting music poured into Britain. Little Richard, Fats Domino, Carl Perkins, Frankie Lymon and the Teenagers, and Bill Dogget all had hits in that year. Rock and roll was here to stay and would never die. Also, at the end of 1956, a young actor was to meet his death in a car crash after making only three films. James Dean posthumously achieved cult status overnight, although only his first film, "Rebel Without A Cause", had been seen in Britain.

Terry had consigned his Ted suits to the back of the wardrobe and, searching for a new style, alternated between the black leather jacket of Brando in "The Wild One" (banned in Britain, but plenty of movie stills in print) and Dean's red windcheater from Rebel. Tee shirts were available in the army and navy stores, but blue jeans were hard to find, and Levis unobtainable.

During his lunch breaks, at the print works Terry sat in the canteen, drinking sweet tea, feeding his spots with cake and biscuits provided by his mum, and listening to the other apprentices talking about beer and *girls*, sport and *girls*, films and *girls*, and giving graphic descriptions of their sexual exploits with *girls*, more the product of fevered imaginations than actual experience. Two of the young men about town enlivened the conversation with a different topic, which made Terry sit up and take notice. Davey Craig and Bill Price were a couple of likely lads with frank, open faces, full of energy and fond of a laugh. The subject they were discussing was hitch hiking to the many youth hostels in the surrounding countryside of Durham and Northumberland. Every weekend scores of young girls and boys could be seen on the North, South and West roads out of Newcastle, rucksacks on their backs and thumbs out, leaving the close packed houses and dirty factories behind, heading for fresh air and freedom. Thanks to Dave and Bill's encouragement Terry was soon one of them, and it was the beginning of a great adventure. In 1956, hitch hiking was an easy and acceptable means of travel. Traffic was light and moved slowly, hitch hikers were not looked upon as potential murderers and the many rules on overcrowding cars and travelling on backs of lorries and trailers had yet to be passed. There were youth hostels situated in beautiful secluded spots, hostels of all shapes and sizes in converted barns, old country houses, wooden chalets, Nissen huts and terraced houses. Some with wardens living in, others where you picked the key up from the local shop. Terry made his way to them in cars without brakes, lorries belching smoke, in sports cars and family saloons, on bales of hay in the back of a trailer hauled by a tractor, or clinging for dear life to the back of some crazy biker testing his Triumph Bonneville to its limits and determined to make him shit himself with fear.

It was not uncommon for an open backed lorry with no load to stop and pick up as many hitch hikers as possible, just to get some weight on its tail to stop it from bouncing. This was an exciting, interesting, but dangerous way of meeting your fellows in the hitch hiking fraternity. It was always advisable not to accept one of these lifts with anything approaching a full bladder as "piss calls" were at the whim of the driver. Should the desire to urinate become

**City kids
on the road.**

overwhelming there was only one answer, to be undertaken when need turned to desperation. This involved shuffling to the tail gate of the trailer and - this is where you found out who your friends were - with someone hanging onto your belt, pissing off the back - the better endowed were at particular advantage on these occasions. Raucous cheers would accompany the whole operation from the boys and giggles from the girls. But once accomplished it gave you a spurious status among your fellow passengers, tinged with envy if their own bladders were at bursting point

Almost every weekend Terry would find out from Bill, Davy and their friends what the destination was to be and they would all contrive, by whatever means possible, to get there, with a bit of friendly rivalry as to who made it first. Boys hitched alone or in pairs, girls would set off in twos, threes or even fours, and still arrive first. Terry soon found that if you could persuade one of the girls to travel with you this was the ideal combination for appealing to a greater cross-section of potential chauffeurs. Standing by some lonely highway waiting for your next lift evoked a camaraderie which broke down the barriers between the sexes and rendered the sexual role-playing people indulge as in superfluous. He discovered he was able to form deep bonds with young women, some of whom would remain his friends for many years to come. It took a girl with little or no regard for convention to don trousers and boots, pick up a rucksack and head for the open road. They were independent, funny, interesting and, with their tight jeans, faces free of makeup and windswept hair, it has to be said, absolutely bloody gorgeous.

Travelling in this way Terry discovered the beauty of his native county and the surrounding counties of Berwickshire, Westmorland, Cumberland and Durham, heading for hostels as far apart as Coldingham, over the Scottish border, and Barnard Castle, in Teesdale. The youth hostels were frequented by a good proportion of genuine hikers, climbers, cyclists and ramblers desiring to commune with nature. Although those young, working class, city kids shared the same desires, their main preoccupations were hedonistic in nature. Drinking and looking for girls were the main driving forces, so much so that climbing into, and accidentally breaking, a window after the strictly imposed curfew of 10pm put an end to Terry's youth hostelling days, but not to his travelling.

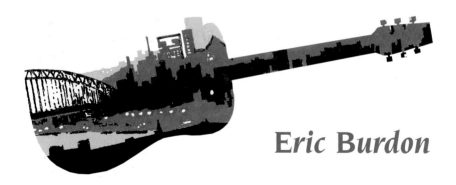

Eric Burdon

This was a time when people actually received proper training in their chosen trade, and, one day a week, Terry attended The Newcastle College of Art and Industrial Design, situated on the corner of Stowell Street and Bath Lane. This building also housed the full-time graphic arts students. Most of his fellow printers considered these arty types a load of middle class twits, but Terry found them interesting, especially as they included girls who had long hair and wore bizarre clothes. The boys too tended to dress in a fashion more akin to his own taste. By now, he had gravitated towards lumber jackets, Wrangler blue jeans and cowboy boots. Thursday was his day for attending printing college, this was also the day Melody Maker came out, and Terry would buy it in order to sound authoritative about what was happening in the music business. At that time, the paper included as much jazz as it did popular music.

This was January 1957, and although there was still plenty of rock & roll around, Tommy Steele and Guy Mitchell were competing for number one with a song called Singing the Blues. This song was as far away from being blues as was possible, which was just as well, since neither singer was capable of singing the blues.

It was lunchtime and Terry was sitting alone in the college canteen drinking orange coloured tea and tucking into a pork sandwich from Bowyers pork shop on Bath Lane. The Melody Maker lay before him and he perused it with interest, completely oblivious of his surroundings. The light filtering through the grubby windows and illuminating the newsprint was suddenly blocked out by someone's shadow. Terry looked up. Smiling down on him was the pockmarked face of a young man who would one day sing the blues with as much fervour and conviction as any black man or woman.

"Wi were wondering where yi got yah boots from," he said, gazing down with covetous eyes at the black, tooled leather, cowboy boots protruding from the turned-up cuffs of Terry's blue jeans. Recognising the stocky, dark haired figure as one of a coterie of art students who had often attracted his attention, he was flattered by their interest. Crossing one leg over the other to expose more of the footwear under discussion, Terry replied, "A great little shop on Blackett Street, Freemans army stores."

There followed a conversation about jeans, boots and army store regalia, and, as the Melody Maker lay before them, the state of British pop music, both deploring the efforts of Frankie Vaughan and Pat Boone, and extolling the virtues of Presley and Fats Domino.

As Eric Burdon ambled back to his fellows to report on the boots, Terry watched him go, and resolved to make every effort to get to know this interesting young man and his equally unusual friends.

Although alone that day, Terry's usual companion in the canteen was fellow apprentice George Stoves, another music lover who concentrated all his attention on pop. George's mother played piano in a semi-professional capacity and, although he made no mention of the fact, George was also a competent pianist. Together they met three young printers who worked at Cut Out Cartons, a large company producing the brightly printed boxes for the burgeoning packaging industry soon to envelop us all in a sea of cardboard. John (Chunky) Bourne, a large, grinning figure whose nickname described him perfectly, Brian (Spike) Tulip, another self-descriptive nickname, his black crew cut standing up like a hedgehog's bristles, and Alan Carr, small and dark, whose love of music was to influence them all. Such was his enthusiasm that most of his spare cash went on importing American records, mainly from the Chess Chicago catalogue. Most teenagers considered themselves pretty hip if they bought pop singles. Here was a guy importing albums by artistes such as Bo Diddley, Chuck Berry, The Flamingos, The Moonglows, and many other black groups not heard in Britain. In fact, in America itself, the majority of the music produced by the black members of that society was not recorded by the major record companies or heard on mainstream radio. Most of this great music was recorded by small independent companies and only played on "race" stations whose audience was almost exclusively black. For a group of white, working class kids in a Northern industrial city to be avid fans of music emanating from the black ghettos of America was unusual but, as passing time would show, not unique.

In retrospect, it seems amazing that popular music exerted such an influence on the lives of young people, as there was little opportunity to hear any. Radio Luxembourg was the only music station reaching Britain, and its signal was often difficult to tune into. The BBC had a couple of record request shows and Saturday Club, the one show catering to the youth market. The "Six-Five Special" was to appear on television that year, featuring resident band Don Lang and his Frantic Five, a pathetic copy of Bill Haley's already watered-down version of black American jump music, like Louie Jordan's Tympany Five. However, the programme did feature live bands, and proved to be very influential. The other, much more convivial, way of listening to music was on pub juke boxes, often a much more accurate reflection of popular taste.

Chunky and his mates seemed to have acquired an intimate knowledge of the more insalubrious hostelries in Newcastle, discovered in their relentless search for good juke boxes (i.e. those with the most rock & roll). The venue for the following evening was to be the Golden Tiger at the bottom of Pilgrim Street, where you could play 5 records for a shilling and the manager was a queer.

Terry and George were invited. The boys had never encountered a homosexual, or even used the word, although they had seen it bandied about in the gutter press, so Vivien was quite a revelation. Homosexuality was still against the law in 1957 and homophobia an unquestioned attitude. To be an outrageous camp queen with make up and dyed blonde hair was to be a very brave person indeed, but Vivien did just that, and carried it off with panache. His cheerful, often filthy, badinage with his customers kept him safe, backed up by his reputation for being very handy with his fists. Working at a scrap metal merchants by day and a pub by night made him hard first, homosexual second. Camping and coercing, serving and serenading, keeping a lot of balls in the air at the same time, as he would pun, made him a well liked barman. Vivien went on to run his own pub, The Azure Blue in Gateshead, and turned it into a popular, successful hostelry. Sadly, he was to be stabbed to death in a drunken fracas at the pub, a sad and needless end for a popular and well-loved character.

The ambience of The Golden Tiger was definitely one of sleaze, with a fair proportion of whores, drunken soldiers and general deadbeats among the clientele, and the five young men wallowed in decadence and draught Bass. Friday nights on the juke box trail became the high point of the week, and together they sampled the wares of the Old George, the Black Boy, the Royal Court Grill, the Cumberland Arms and many more down to earth city pubs where good beer was the first priority, and comfort the last. On some occasions Terry would miss his last bus and end up staying at Chunky's house, as he had a spare bed and accommodating parents. To a lad brought up in a two-bedroom cottage with no bathroom, the Bourne household seemed middle class. Chunky had his own large bedroom with two single beds, a record player and, standing in a corner in gleaming splendour, a full set of drums!

By now skiffle was firmly established, Lonnie Donegan kept churning out hits, and the Vipers, Chas McDermitt, and Johnny Duncan all achieved chart success in the genre. Dozens of other groups were signed up to record deals, and hundreds of kids throughout the country were getting together to play the music just for fun. Why couldn't Chunky, Spike, George and Terry do the same? Chunky had the drums, the ever-reticent George Stoves admitted to owning a guitar and Spike was working on his parents to buy him one. Terry, doubting whether his aptitude for music merited any financial investment, opted for tea chest bass, easy to make although hard to carry around. No one had a tape recorder so they hired one, and rehearsals took place every Tuesday at George's house when his parents were out. These rehearsals consisted of buying loads of beer, running through a few numbers and then playing them back while drinking. Needless to say, more time was spent drinking than playing, but some progress was made and eventually they had learned enough songs to try for a few gigs. The band was called "The Jesters" and thanks to sympathetic friends with cloth ears, they did get some work at weddings and birthday parties. Owning no transport of their own meant that all journeys had to be undertaken by bus, Chunky confining his drum kit to snare drum, hi-hat and cymbal, or quite often a stagger carrying the instruments, and Terry abandoned several tea chest basses over this period.

One night, walking along Walker Road past a pub called The Scrogg, a determined and potentially violent drunk insistent on "having a go" on their instruments confronted them. As the bass was the most dispensable, and Terry was sick of hauling it through the icy streets, they instructed the drunk in bass plonking and left him to it. A mile down the road they could still hear the dull thud echoing down the cold, empty streets. The bass was never replaced, and the cold weather soon dampened the determination and dedication necessary to keep a group together. Spike and Terry's flirtation with the musical life was over, but George and Chunky were to carry on playing for many years to come.

The pub crawling continued, but, apart from that, the main preoccupation with this crowd was finding somewhere to have a party. Parties meant being able to play your own records, much cheaper drink, a camp bed and, if all went well, an abundance of female companions. If someone's parents were away from home for a weekend party plans soon developed. Word went round to a select few with strict instructions to keep it quiet to avoid gatecrashers. If it was really well organised a kitty would collected and crates of beer bought in the afternoon with a few Cherry B's and Babychams for the prospective girls. Then the difficult part, the quest for beautiful Babycham drinkers of the opposite sex who could stay out late or hopefully all night. Parties without girls were invariably depressing, beer quaffing failures. With this in mind, no effort was spared to recruit as many as possible. So there were always girls, never enough, few who could be persuaded into the bedrooms, but sufficient to create the degree of sexual energy needed to make a party swing. But they never seemed to drink the Cherry B.

Chas Chandler

The spring of 1957 found actor heart-throb Tab Hunter at the no. 1 spot with a schmaltzy ballad called "Young Love", but rock and roll was well represented by Little Richards "Long Tall Sally" and "Lucille", both in the top ten. Easter was approaching and Chunkie's parents were going away for the weekend. A party was on the horizon. Terry managed to persuade a girl from his own village, a regular travelling companion on the last bus home, that this was her opportunity to meet some sophisticated city folk. Hazel, a small, cheerful redhead with an independent streak already worked in Newcastle and was bored with village life, so she told the appropriate lies to her parents and agreed to stay out all night.

The party was a success with more than enough drink and even some food laid on. After a great deal of the former and a little of the latter Terry steered Hazel towards the bedroom. Somehow the brown ale interfered with his plans, and he woke up with only a lipstick-smeared face and the dusty smell of face powder to remind him of his lost opportunity. The party was still going on downstairs. He headed for the bathroom, quickly washed, cleaned his teeth, combed his hair and staggered downstairs ready to start again. When he reached the hall the doorbell was ringing, competing with the noise inside. Only three kinds of people would be ringing that bell so late at night, gatecrashers, angry neighbours or police. Terry felt obliged to open it.

Outlined against the privet hedge stood two very tall blonde youths. Terry's mind raced, how could he turn away gatecrashers as large as this on his own? Then he noticed the guitars; each carried a black guitar case, a sure-fired guarantee for a party invitation. The taller of the two loomed out of the darkness and Terry recognised Chas Chandler wreathed in smiles and brown ale fumes, "Where's Chunky?" he asked, "wha invited."

Terry indicated the door leading to the front room. The pounding of a full drum kit accompanying a Fats Domino record made it pretty clear where Chunky was, so they entered the room, guitars to the fore. Chas and his mate Gordon Cleghorn were already pretty well known, so Chunky didn't bother with introductions, just sat them down and supplied some beer. Terry walked over to Hazel who, her small form ensconced in a huge armchair, (usually the sole preserve of Mr Bourne senior), was sipping a beer and watching the proceedings with interest. The amused but welcoming smile on her elfin face reassured Terry and she was soon snuggled down on his knee.

By this time Chas and Clegg, with an unconvincing show of reluctance, had bowed to requests to "give us a tune!" and the instruments were being disinterred from the shining black cases. What they produced from the red velvet linings were a matching pair of Framus Black Rose guitars inlaid with black and red mother of pearl. The envy in the faces of the aspiring guitarists in the audience intensified when it became apparent that the duo could actually tune up and play them. They were soon going through their repertoire of skiffle and rock and roll with Everly Brothers songs predominating, accompanied by Chunkie's enthusiastic drumming and the massed chorus of assembled drunks. Mindful of the neighbours and the potential wrath of his parents Chunkie finally called a halt to the proceeding and those who lived nearby set off to walk home. For the rest a pile of blankets and quilts were provided, and Terry grabbed some bedding for Hazel and himself and sought out a draught free corner. Deciding he had done enough wrestling for the evening he held her tenderly and they drifted off to sleep together.

When they awoke in the half-light of early morning, still in each other's arms, his consideration was rewarded. Without any coaxing Hazel gently masturbated his early morning erection while he kissed her soft mouth, trying desperately not to allow his beery breath to sully her delicate nostrils, and wondering all the while why he was filled with the most desire while he was at his least desirable.

Sleep reclaimed them and when they next awoke the curtains were open and modern jazz emanated softly from the record player. Chunkie was clattering glasses in the kitchen. Gradually the assorted bodies littering the living room returned to the land of the living, filling the air with a morning chorus of moans, curses and imprecations against the dawn. The Bourne household was unique among Terry's acquaintances in that they made real percolated coffee. Drawn by the wonderful aroma, Terry and Hazel joined Chunkie and pitched in with the washing up. They were rewarded with huge cups of the hot, milky, hangover-curing beverage. Those not too wounded by over-indulgence in alcohol made haste to return the house to some kind of normality. Windows were opened and the tortured whine of the vacuum cleaner urged them on. It was Sunday morning and the motivation for this burst of activity was simple. The British licensing laws decreed that the pubs should only open between 12 noon and 2pm, and here was a bunch of young people who needed a drink.

Pubs on Sunday lunchtimes were usually populated exclusively by males, so when the party-goers entering the environs of The Black Horse, Longbenton that morning included a fair sprinkling of vibrant females the dominoes stopped clicking and a darts player almost missed double top. However, the landlord was happy to serve them and they were soon reliving and exaggerating last night's events amidst gales of laughter and good humour. For Terry this was often the best part of a party, and he and Hazel drank in the beer and the atmosphere with equal gusto. Eventually it was time to take her home, so they caught the big yellow double-decker bus to the Haymarket bus station, were they could connect with the rural bus service, to carry them back to their home village of Cramlington. As the bus wended its way home, they both agreed that they would much rather live in Newcastle and swore they would make the move some day. Eventually the lunchtime beer had its soporific effect and they fell asleep in each others arms, to be awoken by the friendly conductress when they reached their stop. They parted with many promises to keep in touch, but it would prove to be some time before they met again.

Shot Gun Wedding

A few weeks later Terry was invited to the wedding reception of fellow printer Dougie Pomeray. He had got his girl friend in "the family way" as the old euphemism has it and was about to do the decent thing. Dougie was a popular boy and had invited a good crowd, including Davie Craig, Bill Price, Chunkie Bourne, and Chas Chandler. The main attraction was that Dougie was friendly with a rock-and-roll band from Whitley Bay called The Wildcats, who were building up quite a reputation. Terry's problems of getting home on the last bus were solved by Bill offering him a bed for the night, and, as Terry was in unrequited love with Bill's sister Anne, he jumped at the chance.

The venue was at Monkseaton so, on the appointed day, Terry boarded the train for the coast along with Davey, Bill and his sister Anne plus her two friends Marie and Jean. The reception was in a church hall so, once they had located it, they headed for the nearest pub, only to find the rest of the guests already in residence, including the bridegroom. Wedding receptions could be dreary affairs, especially when held in ancient draughty buildings, still clothed in the austere browns and creams of the war years. When they finally made it to the church hall they found the band tuning up and were agreeably surprised to find several trestle tables laden down with drink of every kind, but no food. The Wildcats launched into "Long Tall Sally" with professional ease, followed swiftly by Be-Bop-A-Lula. It was rock-and-roll all the way and soon the dance floor was full. Dougie, who had missed no opportunity of taking a celebratory drink during the course of the day, was dancing with his heavily pregnant wife in the badly uncoordinated manner of the classic drunk. Terry persuaded Anne onto the floor, her perfect timing and fluid movements filling him with delight.

As the night progressed it became apparent that the party had acquired some gate-crashers. Five teddy boys were clustered round the beer table and only Dougie knew that they were not invited. He lurched his way over to ask them to leave and was greeted with a wall of animosity. In time honoured fashion an argument ensued and Dougie's mates were picking up on the tension-laden atmosphere, until inevitably a punch was thrown. The assailant was the leader of the Teds, a big swarthy lad wearing a dark green suit and the recipient was the unfortunate Dougie, who was in no state to look after himself. What possessed these five young men to cause trouble when they were so heavily outnumbered was a mystery that no one wasted any time pondering over. Chas downed his pint, then downed the leader with a couple of punches, while Chunkie set about the first one to come to hand. Two of the smaller lads broke away and headed for what they fondly assumed was the rear exit, pursued by Chas and Terry, who knew it was the toilet. When they entered there was no sign of the lads but one cubicle was locked. Chas gave the plasterboard wall an experimental punch and felt it give. He punched it again. Terry joined in and soon they had created a sizeable hole, exposing the two cowering youths. Deciding they had suffered enough Chas and Terry left them to it and returned to the hall, where their compatriots had been disposed of through the front door.

The band, no doubt familiar with the occasional outbreak of violence on the dance floor, had continued to play. The trouble was soon forgotten and the party carried on, although Dougie was now having a verbal fight with his young wife. Probably, the first of many.

As the consumption of beer continued a few of the guests began to regret the lack of food. Terry volunteered to make the trip to a nearby pork shop, for saveloy and pease pudding, or pork sandwiches. Pork or "dip" shops were as popular as fish and chip shops at that time and tended to stay open later. As he waited in the noisy, boozy queue he noticed a line of meat hooks hanging within reach. Having recently seen "On The Waterfront" his imagination carried him off to the docks of New York and the stevedores with their loading hooks. He became the other Terry Molloy, the character played by Marlon Brando, facing up to Johnny Friendly's gang in the hold of the ship, hook in hand. He reached out and slipped one of the hooks under his jacket onto his belt loop.

On leaving the shop he was confronted with real life, in the shape of three of the lads recently ejected from the wedding, their colourful, if grubby Ted suits standing out in the drab light of the street lamps. As they swaggered down the street towards him, the expressions on their faces confirmed his suspicion that he had been recognised. He felt his sphincter tighten with fear, but he walked towards them trying to look nonchalant. "Hello lads, fancy a saveloy." As he spoke he took his parcel of food in both hands like a rugby ball and feinted to the left then wheeled to the right and slid past them. The only sport he had any prowess in was the 100 yard sprint, this and pure terror lent him the speed to escape. Fortunately, smoking untipped cigarettes from an early age had not put his would-be assailants in shape to win any races and he was soon running free.

On his return to the hall he handed out the food, making sure everyone had a full account of his adventure. He sat with Anne embroidering on his story while they listened to the band together. His previous experience of live music had been almost exclusively jazz. This was the first time he had seen a genuine rock-and-roll band made up of kids of his own age and he could not have been more impressed. It made him realise that his own tentative attempts at playing skiffle were always doomed to failure, as he lacked the natural talent and total dedication to reach such a standard. He was particularly impressed by lead guitarist Hilton Valentine ripping out the solos with style and panache, to the worshipful encouragement of the females in the audience. This was a rock-and-roll star just waiting to happen.

Time for the last train home was looming large as the band played its final encore. Bill, Terry, Marie and Anne went to say their goodbyes - Dave and Jean having slipped away earlier - and found the groom incoherent and his young wife in tears.

"That's not the last time she'll cry over that bastard."

Anne observed dryly, "He's nothing but trouble."

This epitaph delivered, they headed for the Monkseaton station. As they approached its handsome Victorian portals, who should be waiting for them but their ugly Edwardian adversaries. "This is gettin boring", said Terry.

"Aye", agreed Bill, and then to the three teds, "just let's take the lasses in the station, then w'ill sort this out."

In an uncharacteristic display of gallantry, the leader acquiesced with a grunt and they ushered the girls into the station and turned to face the music.

"Yi still got that hook, Terry?" asked Bill, producing a bottle of beer from his pocket, saved for the train journey.

"Aye", answered Terry, unhooking it from his belt loop and taking it in his right hand. By now the pair had consumed enough alcohol to be without fear and they swaggered out together. At the sight of the weapons the teds began to bluster and would have been calling for fair play, if they had known the meaning of the phrase. The two boys advanced and the teds retreated, as the train could be heard pulling into the station. Terry and Bill were able to make a run for it and board the train without losing face.

Their relief was palpable, but the trauma was soon forgotten and with that inborn ability for young people to remember pop lyrics the four of them sang in a kind of harmony all the way to the Newcastle Central Station. They walked up from the coast line terminus, past the main line platform, where the locomotive pulling the night train for London was filling the station with noise and vapour, getting up steam for its trip South. Then as now, Geordies were leaving Newcastle for the capital city. Then, the spur was a desire for change, glamour, and excitement, now, it is hopelessness and desperation that drives them from their home city.

Passing through the lofty colonnades of the station they ignored the taxi rank and set off towards the Redeugh bridge, to walk home to Gateshead. As they crossed over the oily waters of the Tyne, Terry became aware of the butchers hook bumping against his thigh. A shudder ran through him at the thought of what could have happened in that drunken affray and hooking it from his belt, he consigned it to the waters, resolving never to carry a weapon again. Hopefully, he slipped his arm around Anne's waist, but she somehow contrived to change to holding hands. Her hand was soft and she did not let go so he contented himself with this contact, and they walked together in companionable silence. After a while he began to hum a tune and they completed the journey singing Frank Sinatra songs, the lyrics of Sammy Cahn and Lorenz Hart ringing out across the silent river.

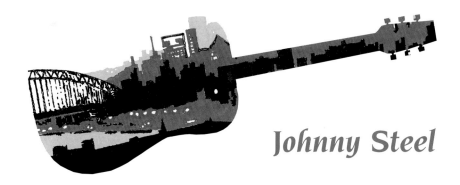

Johnny Steel

Chunky and Spike turned out to be inveterate campers so Terry purchased a small bivouac and joined them in their forays into the lovely countryside of Northumberland, pitching their tents in farmers' fields, on river banks, or among the sand dunes of Seahouses or Bamburgh. Terry preferred the coast, hidden among the dunes on National Trust property where camping was prohibited, drinking with the fishermen on Saturday night, working off their hangovers on Sunday mornings, swimming and sunning naked along the deserted beach, as wild and free as any of the protected creatures in this lovely, lonely nature sanctuary.

Back in Newcastle, an enterprising student by the name of Mike Jeffries opened the University Jazz Club, although under the aegis of the university, the profits all went to Jeffries. This venture was the first step in his career in the world of night clubs and would eventually lead to his management of The Animals, and Jimmy Hendrix. Running on Sunday nights, the venue was the Cordwainers Hall above the Gardeners Arms in Nelson Street. The elegant facade of this building remains, although the interior has been absorbed by the amorphous mass of the Eldon Square shopping experience. A Sunday night club in a city starved of entertainment attracted more of a non-jazz audience with a preponderance of female refugees from the ballrooms, curious to find out what kind of male followed this kind of music. Rock and roll was now firmly established in the charts, Presley, Buddy Holly and Jerry Lee Lewis proving the most dominant, but there was little opportunity to hear the music live and jazz was still the only music to dance to. The grapevine soon filtered the information through to Terry and his mates of excess "talent" at Nelson Street, and regardless of which band was playing this became a regular haunt.

One Sunday evening in spring Terry alighted from the running board of a battered old Citroen of the type he had previously seen only in French films. This was a dream lift that had taken him from the borders of Scotland right to the city centre. Sunburnt and begrimed from a weekend's camping, and with no time to go home, he hefted his rucksack onto one shoulder and headed for Nelson Street. After negotiating his way past the doorman and depositing his rucksack with a bemused cloakroom girl, Terry's thoughts turned to his most urgent need. On the long journey home, hot, tired and dehydrated, one potent image constantly appeared in his imaginings. A tall, cool pint of the splendid, hoppy local brew, Newcastle Exhibition, filled his mind, and he knew just where to assuage his thirst. Collecting a pass out at the door, he stepped into the deserted street. The club was on the second storey and on this warm, balmy evening the sound of the Panama

U
J
C

UNIVERSITY JAZZ CLUB.

Sunday Jazz

20, NELSON STREET, NEWCASTLE.

Membership Card

Jazzmen poured out of the open windows.

Across the street stood the Blackett Arms, incorporated into a Victorian covered market named the Bigg Market. The second storey of the pub was a quiet lounge bar named Simpsons Buffet, discovered by Terry and fellow apprentice George Stoves when they decided to abandon the works canteen and seek somewhere more convivial to eat their lunchtime sandwiches. Terry walked beneath the dark, vaulted arch leading into the market, and, mounting a flight of stairs, soon emerged into the faded splendour of a room that had the appearance of an over-sized Pullman carriage, the rich flowered wallpaper, heavy brocade curtains and uncut moquette upholstery all faded to neutral brown from years of wear and nicotine.

Behind the bar stood a grey-haired matriarch proprietress and Grande Dame of this establishment, her steel rimmed spectacles gleaming dully in the light of the capiz shell wall lamps. Terry ambled up to the bar and leaned heavily on the shining brass rail, "Pint of Ex. please, Mary," he said, smiling into her eyes. Mary Threadgill, with a heart that belied her stern appearance, smiled back, and selected a sparkling glass from the ornate mirrored shelves behind her. She filled it to the brim while Terry licked his lips in anticipation. Handing over his one and sixpence he picked up his pint and looked around the almost deserted room. High-backed, upholstered settles, reminiscent of the seats in old railway carriages surrounded each long, rectangular, cast iron table. He chose the table nearest the bar and gazed with reverence at his pint before taking his first drink.

Another youth appeared from the stairs and, taking a drag on his cigarette, strolled into Mary's vision with an unstudied insouciance that guaranteed his being served without the ignominy of enquiries being made as to his date of birth. Terry eyed the blonde-haired newcomer with interest, recognising him as one of the bunch of students he had first noticed at the art school and had since seen in various pubs and music venues. Johnny Steel purchased his first pint and looked around for somewhere to sit.

"It's packed tonight," said Terry, "ah might just be able to squeeze you in here," patting the seat next to him.

Johnny smiled, and, carrying over his brimming pint, parked himself on the seat next to Terry.

"Been over the jazz club?" asked Johnny, raising his pint to eye level either to check it's clarity or for the sheer, unalloyed pleasure of gazing at a full pint of beer and contemplating the impending gratification of quaffing it down.

"Aye," answered Terry, taking his first drink, "but I seem to have worked up a hell of a thirst."

"Hitch-hiking?" asked Johnny.

"Hitch-hiking," agreed Terry, "ah just got back from Coldingham on the Scottish borders, hell of a weekend."

The stained glass windows were open onto Nelson Street, and from the windows opposite, echoing between the grimy buildings, the pair could hear Joe McMullen's trumpet solo on Big Butter and Egg Man, each mellifluous note ringing out with bell-like clarity. Neither spoke until the solo ended. Although they had just met, they seemed comfortable in each other's presence, a kind of empathy that negated the need for speech. Although they did not realise it at the time, a bond was soon to form, a friendship that would last them a lifetime.

"I wish my trumpet playing was even half as good as that," said Johnny ruefully, raising his cigarette to his lips as if to test out his embouchure.

"You play trumpet?" asked Terry, visibly impressed. "Aye, me and Eric Burdon, you know Burdon?"

Terry nodded in affirmation. "Well, me, him and two other lads, Jimmy Crawford and Alan Sanderson, have been practising together, we've got a name, The Pagan Jazzmen, but that's about it. Tha's me on trumpet, Eric on trombone and vocals, Jimmy on banjo

J. STEEL   Tel. Low Fell 76257

PAGAN
JAZZ MEN

DISCORDANT, SYNCOPATED
MUSIC AT YOUR DISPOSAL

and Blackie (Alan Sanderson) on drums. Ti be honest we're not making a lot of progress." "Still," mused Terry, "It's a start, at least you're doing something."

They carried on discussing traditional jazz and, both being avid readers of sleeve notes and members of jazz book clubs, enjoyed impressing each other with their erudition. The conversation had, inevitably, turned to sex and drink, when they became aware that the music had ceased. "It must be interval time," surmised Johnny.

Terry walked over to the window and gazed down at the club entrance across the street. A phalanx of youth was pouring onto the pavement, mainly lads in smart suits heading for the Gardeners Arms next door, Few girls would consider entering a pub unescorted, so they were left behind to powder their noses, drink soft drinks and discuss the failings of the male sex. After downing a few pints and buoying up each other's confidence with lurid tales of sexual conquest the drunken Lotharios would return, determined to "get off" with someone. It is a tribute to the tolerance and good humour of the female race that some of them would acquiesce and allow themselves to be walked to the bus stop.

The three main bus stations out of Newcastle, Marlborough, Worsick Street and the Haymarket all thronged with teenagers late at night on the weekends. Much garish lipstick was transferred to young men's collars and a great deal of face powder deposited on a great many immaculate lapels before the final bus departed. Occasionally some fortunate lad would find a girl willing to fulfil his dreams of copulation by accompanying him to an unlit back lane for a quick knee trembler. Should such an assignation take place on a Sunday night it would more than likely be a smelly occasion, as bath nights were on Fridays and underwear was rarely changed more than once a week.

Turning from the window Terry headed towards the bar to get the pints in before the rush. He and Johnny were gazing contentedly at the replenished glasses when Eric Burdon, leading a bunch of laughing, jostling figures, appeared from the stairwell. Mary's icy gaze notwithstanding, they bellied up to the brass rail, beer lust in the eye of every boy. After giving them the once-over Mary dispensed the drinks with her usual efficiency, dealing with the wisecracks and general boisterousness with gentle good humour. Terry found himself surrounded by Johnny's friends and was introduced to Burdon, Dave Wilson, Whitey, Jimmy Crawford and Blackie. The conversation flowed like wine, covering music, art, films, books and politics; the whole melee interspersed with insane humour. Terry drank it all in, contributing when he could, but mainly just listening. Here were a crowd with their own language, humour and distinct view of life, and Terry just longed to be part of it.

Eventually someone decided they had better get back to the club and actually hear some jazz before the evening ended, so they all piled over the street, including Terry in the midst, much to his delight. He managed to get in a couple of dances and listen to some more chat before grabbing his rucksack and heading for the last bus home. In the ensuing weeks, he saw a great deal of his new-found friends. Dave Wilson, one of the non-musicians in "The Crowd", took Terry under his wing and invited him to come along wherever they were turning out.

1958 proved to be an uninspiring year for lovers of rock & roll, or any other type of innovative music. Although The Everly Brothers and Jerry Lee Lewis made a few appearances, the top twenty was dominated by the likes of Perry Como, Connie Francis, Vic Damone and an emasculated Elvis Presley singing watered down ballads, tailored to appeal to as wide an audience as possible.

Although the Pagans were trying to play traditional jazz, they seemed to have a healthy interest in every type of music, especially rock & roll and its more esoteric forebears Rhythm & Blues and pure blues. Johnny Steel lived in a large, three-storied house of eccentric design, on Sheriff Hill in Gateshead. A palatial sitting room dominated the second floor and it was here that the band rehearsed. Johnny inspired a certain amount of envy among his fellows, as his parents owned a fish and chip shop, and the boys' hunger for fish and chips was surpassed only by their thirst for beer. Rehearsals followed a fairly predictable pattern. First they ran through a few numbers, sustained by an occasional slug of

Pagan Jazzmen rehearsing

Amber Ale, then they sat drinking and talking about music, and eventually Mrs Steel would arrive with fish and chips to be washed down with more beer. It's doubtful whether the rehearsals would have been so well attended without this culinary treat.

The boys' interest in rock&roll and rhythm & blues began to predominate as their desire to play jazz waned. Eric was neglecting his trombone playing and Johnny began to realise he was never going to be another Bix Biederbeck, so a change of direction became inevitable. To play rock&roll a good strong bass line is essential so Eric decided to try his hand at bass guitar. Without the funds to buy one he utilised the materials at hand and attempted to fashion one from one of the art school's drawing boards. Eventually his natural pragmatism came to the fore and he decided to stick to vocals. This may not have had the cachet of carrying a guitar round town but it was cheaper and a lot more convenient. Blackie aspired towards bass playing and as a working lad could afford to buy one "on tick". Credit restrictions had recently been lifted so it was possible to buy things on the "never-never" as it was termed. Jack Trevor Storey was later to satirise the post war credit boom in his book "Live Now Pay Later". Johnny switched to drums and Jimmy traded in his banjo for a guitar. The Pagan Jazzmen became The Pagans and it would take many nights of dedicated drinking to decide a musical direction and choose suitable material.

The overriding opinion was not to play what was currently fashionable but to follow their own musical tastes. Not a recipe for instant success but they were not looking for or expecting acclaim and did not make the mistake of taking themselves too seriously. Everyone had seen the recent film "The Girl Can't Help It", featuring Eddie Cochran, Little Richard, and Gene Vincent & The Blue Caps. Not surprisingly, the Blue Caps actually wore blue caps and in one scene -no doubt after many takes - flicked their caps off in unison. This seemed to tickle Eric and as it was possible to buy striped county caps in Newcastle, it was decided that this headgear would be the first step towards a band uniform. A second step was never taken.

The Pagans in band uniform

The Squatters

Although there was a lot going on in town to hold Terry's interest, the desire to get out into the countryside was still strong. His work-mates Bill Price and Davey Craig had taken to camping out at Dipton Mill near Hexham. Listening to tales of their exploits soon inspired Terry to dig out his rucksack and get back on the road. Dipton Mill consisted of a pub next a river, a ruined mill and a few cottages. The main attraction was the pub, especially as it had an alcoholic landlord who didn't concern himself too much with licensing hours. They were able to camp in the woods near the river, build huge camp fire and carouse round the flames until the early hours without disturbing anyone. Just to make the weekends complete several of the girls from their youth hostel days joined the throng, adding the extra piquancy of a possible sexual liaison.

One dull Saturday morning Terry alighted from the cab of a battered old furniture wagon onto the cobbled market square of Hexham and, thanking the driver, headed for the bus station. He had no intention of taking a bus but knew that his mates, along with any other owners of rucksacks, would dump their gear there prior to having a wander round town before setting off for their final destination. Terry slung his rucksack among the rest and using it as a back rest sprawled out on the pavement to watch the world go by.

The local people going about their leisurely Saturday morning business were interspersed by the bright anoraks of ramblers, cyclists and youth hostellers all out to enjoy the countryside. Among the many city folk who appreciated the bucolic charm of Northumberland was one group Terry knew of by reputation but of whom he had only caught an occasional glimpse. They were known as The Squatters. Depending on your point of view, The Squatters were a group of individualists, non-conformists living the outdoor life in their own unique way, or a bunch of drunken lunatics cutting a swathe of mayhem and madness through sleepy rural life. Terry suspected that many of the lurid tales about them were apocryphal rather than factual, but strolling towards him was someone who could put the record straight.

The figure approaching him wore the cleated boots, folded down white socks, and carried the commando rucksack of a hiker, but his wild black hair, with sideburns, black leather jacket and torn black jeans were redolent of the pictures of Hell's Angels he had seen in American magazines. Getting to his feet he greeted the newcomer with a nervous grin. The fearsome apparition smiled back a perfect set of teeth gleaming out from his blue jowls. "How yi doing kid ?" "Ahm Hank "

Terry gave his name, relieved to find that Hank was not unfriendly, and it soon became apparent that he was in the company of one of the infamous squatters. As they were both waiting for their respective mates they stood and chatted, Hank regaling the young innocent with tales of his exploits. He completed his national service as long ago as the length of his hair, and his last tour of duty involved fighting E.O.K.A. terrorists in Cyprus. His army training taught him unarmed combat, the use of fire-arms and various methods of killing people quickly and silently. All useful skills for a young man living in the slums of Gateshead.

Standing together casually eyeing up the local talent, they both noticed a slim dark-haired girl heading towards the sweet shop across the street. She had a pretty if slightly over made up face and wore a camel haired coat and brown shoes with stack heels. Terry judged her to be about sixteen years old. A gleam of recognition appeared in Hanks eyes, "Watch this kid, ahm ganna shag that".

So saying he set off across the road in time to meet the girl coming out of the shop clutching a bag of sweets. They set off up the road together chatting like old friends, Hank helping himself to sweets. There was still no sign of Terry's friends, and feeling somehow that Hank expected him to be there on his return he bought himself a newspaper and settled down to wait. Around half an hour later Hank returned grinning triumphantly. "Had ti take her out i town, little shed thing, bit muddy, shi's a bit tight, couldn't get it all in" he boasted. Terry stared at him in disbelief while trying to appear blasé. The muddy knees of the black jeans confirmed the story. The girl who had split away from Hank as they approached the bus station had mud all over the back of her camel haired coat. He wondered how she would explain that to her mam! He was to witness this phenomenon often, apparently innocent young girls allowing themselves to be casually screwed by brutes like Hank who had all the finesse of a battering ram. Certainly such a cavalier approach never worked for him.

As he stood reflecting on this mystery a bus from Newcastle drew in. "Here's the lads" said Hank. A miscellany of folk disgorged from the vehicle and finally the group occupying the rear seats disembarked. First to emerge was big Alex, resplendent in cut off Air Force great coat and turned down wellies, followed by Animal Hogg, a huge ragged figure with wild long hair and beard. Next came Spud, skinny blonde-haired, face ravaged by acne, wearing a duffel coat that looked as if it had been buried in the garden for a fortnight. It had in fact been given that treatment - to give it character. Last and most incongruous of all came Noddy. His hair still worn teddy boy style with a roll of greasy curls on his forehead, dressed in a once elegant, brown, double breasted coat with astrakhan collar now improved by the addition of a knotted string belt. Somewhere on the journey the pressure of lunchtime boozing had become too much for Noddy's bladder. As the bus driver had refused to stop he was forced to take alternative action. Removing his welly he had utilised it as an impromptu urinal. Thus relieved, he returned it to his foot completing the journey with an empty bladder and a soggy sock. He now paraded the streets of Hexham welly in hand, wet sock making woolly footprints on the pavement, the soggy sounds accompanied by raucous laughter from the rest of the crowd and not a few of the passing shoppers.

At this point three motor bikes cruised into town, their riders wearing short leather jackets, blue jeans, high laced boots and colourful neckerchiefs, but no helmets or gloves. Jimmy Chambers, Joe Chambers, and Davey Crockett parked their bikes on the cobbles and joined the rest. Despite their beat-up apparel the whole bunch owned expensive ex-commando rucksacks in good condition apart from the fact that, without exception, the side pockets appeared to have rotted or been eaten away by something. These rucks joined the pile already cluttering the bus station and without discussion, like a troop of mercenary soldiers they crossed the road towards The Royal Hotel. Hank called back to Terry, "Haway kid, come with us, yi might get a few laughs".

The Royal Hotel is an old coaching inn with a central arch through

Fashion parade
left to right
Hutchie, Red
Alex & Spud

which coaches once rattled to the stable yard behind. Terry would never have considered using such a grand place, especially dressed as he was, but the ragged squad marched through with great aplomb and were soon draped over the upholstery of a small smoke room tucked away at the rear of the building. Once everyone had a pint in front of them they turned their attention to Terry.

"Who's ya mate Hank?" demanded Alex, foam clinging to his black beard, demonic eyes glittering under bushy brows. Hank turned and surveyed Terry's short combed-forward red hair and freckled countenance .

"Yi heard of Sunblest Sammy, well this is Sunblest Terry ", he said grinning at his sudden inspiration. Sunblest Sammy was a cartoon character created to advertise Sunblest bread. So now Terry had a nickname which stuck to him from that day hence. "Here's to Sunblest" hollered Spud raising his glass.

The rest ignored him, turning their attention to Animal Hogg who was at the tiny hatch of a bar having some discussion with the plump young blonde barmaid who obviously knew him. Eventually the girl withdrew to return ten minutes later with two beer trays piled high with pies, sausage rolls, vol-au-vents and rather tired looking sandwiches obviously left over from some buffet or other. The goodies were seized upon with general approbation and Spud proposed a toast to barmaids everywhere, with the devout hope that he would someday marry one. Three o-clock closing quickly arrived and although they managed to squeeze in an extra pint after time they eventually spilled out onto the street and a world that looked far rosier than before.

Back at the bus station they casually began to go through the other hikers' rucksacks extracting any tins of food that took their fancy.

"These lads' mams give them too much scran," mused Noddy.

"It'll only weigh them down", he pronounced as he strapped a tin of corned beef and two tins of beans and sausages into his decaying side pockets. Foraging complete, they set off for the river to 'stash' the gear. Situated down river from the manicured lawns and flower beds of the immediate river banks was a wood yard bounded by a high wooden fence. In a few minutes they were over the fence and surveying the huge trestles on which pine logs lay stacked to season. The space underneath made an ideal shelter. The rucks were duly slung underneath ready for the evening and they headed back into town.

As they shambled through the busy afternoon streets with Noddy and Spud acting as self appointed clowns keeping them all laughing, they attracted a lot of attention from passers by. Terry began to enjoy himself, swaggering along with the rest, basking in the notoriety they engendered, until he caught sight of himself in a shop window looking rather foolish. He realised that their self assured walk and unconventional behaviour did not stem from any desire to show off. In fact they seemed to be totally oblivious of the effect they had on other people, but ploughed on regardless of the consequences. Terry decided just to be himself and enjoy the ride.

Big Alex led the way up a narrow alley to a tiny dance studio. The proprietor had decided to supplement his income by opening a disco, or "having a record session" as the term discotheque was not yet in common parlance. As they walked in, "Ma he's making eyes at me" was blaring out. It never occurred to Terry that there was any possibility of gaining entry given their sartorial condition. However the manager appeared to know Alex and welcomed them all in on payment of 1/6d. Soon they were drinking milk shakes to the sound of "The Chordettes" singing "Lollipop", looking incongruous by the light of the mirrored ball revolving in the centre of the room.

The rest of the clientele consisted mainly of pubescent girls too young even for the lascivious Hank to consider. Obviously a student of human nature, the manager changed the tone of the music and when "A wonderful time up there" by Pat Boone began to play they headed for the door.

It was almost opening time and at 6 o-clock Animal was banging on the door of the Turks Head, demanding entry. After one drink they moved on to The Coach and Horses and then, to Terry's amazement, to the lounge bar of The Royal Hotel. There was some reticence on the part of the barmaid but she reluctantly served them. They were soon firmly ensconced, happily appreciating the talent of the resident piano player, his huge sausage-like fingers and fly-away left hand banging out songs from the shows. All was well until Spud, with an elaborate bow, asked Noddy to join him in a dance. Alex and Animal joined them and they were soon embroiled in a terpsichorean improvisation for wellies that would have delighted lovers of dance throughout the world. Authority in the form of a diminutive bespectacled manager finally asked them to leave. Alex's wild eyes twinkled mischievously but, possibly mindful of future supplies of pork pies, he acquiesced and danced his way out, his hairy partner still clutching a bottle of brown.

The rest of the company followed suit and after executing a few twirls on the high street, they set off up the road towards "The Criterion". This pub was more suitable for persons of their demeanour, being rather spartan in decor but containing a well stocked and very loud juke box. Spud headed straight for it and put on Jerry Lee Lewis's "Whole lotta shakin", "At the hop" by Danny and the Juniors and "Good Golly Miss Molly" by "Little Richard", three songs guaranteed to wake everyone up. So the evening went with a swing, Spud collecting everyone's money to feed the juke box, never failing to select his favourite "Whole lotta shakin'". The rest of the clientele, mainly of a similar age and only slightly better dressed than "the lads", seemed to enjoy the music, if not the company But drink is a mind-altering substance and one of the locals, a youth with greasy black hair, greasy black suit, and greasy black string tie decided he was sick of "Jerry Lee Lewis". He took hold of Spud's arm as he stepped up to make another selection.

"Hey kid, put sumick fuckin different on this time," he bellowed, squeezing the skinny biceps viciously. Noddy was on his feet in an instant and with the practised ease of someone used to humping sacks of coal, placed the complainant firmly on top of the juke box.

"Is that different enough fo yi, arsehole?" he enquired with a characteristic throaty chuckle changing to booming laughter which infected the whole room, including the luckless lads' mates. The music critic would have been wise to have laughed off the incident but rashly he leapt from his perch and made for Noddy with fists flying. This was when he learned that Noddy had not been named after a creation of Enid Blyton's with a penchant for hats with bells on and a friend named Big Ears. Noddy's head snaked out and connected with a bone crunching thud. His opponent found himself on the floor among the fag ends and spilt beer, blood gently seeping from his rapidly swelling nose. His mates dragged him back to his seat muttering imprecations but took no action. Discretion being the better part of valour, they quickly drank up.

As they were leaving, the opening chords of "Whole lotta shakin" burst forth from the juke box, to cheers from Noddy and co. The evening took its drunken course and when time was called, the landlord, who had missed or totally ignored the violence, appeared from behind the small hatch that served the room and chivvied them out with a total lack of bonhomie or charm. What he lacked in charm he made up for in greed, and was easily persuaded to sell some carry outs. The bottles were placed in a crisp box and much to his surprise entrusted to Terry. As they emerged into open air it occurred to him that the lads knew what would be waiting for them and that's why he had been given the task.

Outside stood Noddy's erstwhile sparring partner along with, it seemed to Terry, the scourings of Hexham's roughest pubs. Most fights begin with much posturing and obscene verbals, but The Squatters dispensed with such preliminaries. The Chambers brothers and Crockett, thinking only of their bikes, punched their way through the mob and sped down the street. Alex and Animal laid about them, seemingly impervious to the few punches that did connect. Noddy, Hank and Spud stayed near Terry, downing every assailant for practical rather than protective reasons - he had the beer.

The three bikers finding their bikes intact, kick-started them into life and roared back down the street at full throttle, headlights blazing. The psychological effect on the mob was dramatic, they scattered and the bikes slewed round in a tight turn to make another run. This time the riders leapt off and joined in the affray. As the battle increased in ferocity a familiar sound gradually impinged on the senses of the combatants, the clamorous bell of a "Black Maria" growing louder by the minute. The taciturn landlord had obviously made a phone call and, as the Hexham police force was not overworked, they were on their way.

As the thought of a night in the cells appealed to no-one, all hostilities ceased and escape became the dominant urge. Hank grabbed Terry.

"This way", he said, heading towards the sound of the bell, "Just walk slowly."

Spud, seeing which way the beer was going, fell in step beside them. The black police van sped past heading for the source of the trouble, arriving in time to see three powerful motor-bikes each carrying two people roaring off in the direction of Newcastle. Those too drunk or incapacitated to make a run for it were loaded into the back of the van with a great show of bravado by the psyched-up bobbies.

Hank and Spud led Terry down a labyrinth of passages leading eventually to the river. On reaching the wood yard they found the rest already there, the bikes concealed under a weeping willow and a fire flickering into life. The beer was descended upon without ceremony and as the flames grew higher they toasted their feet, and each other, on what they considered to be a pretty successful evening. Eventually the talk died away and exhaustion set in. Terry proved to be the only one with a torch to light the way over the wood yard fence and under the huge trestles where they climbed fully clothed into their sleeping bags.

Sleep soon overtook him and he slumbered soundly until the early hours when a repetitive sound began to gnaw into his brain gradually bringing him to wakefulness. He was using his rucksack as a pillow and the noise seemed to vibrate through the heavy canvas. After some sleepy fumbling he located his torch, and the light illuminated the twitching whiskers, startled eyes, and yellow teeth of a huge rat. A wave of scrotum-tightening terror of an intensity he had never before experienced, paralysed his body. Transfixed for a moment, the rat turned and ran, along with several of its fellows, their hunched backs and vile tails illuminated in the beam of the torch. Heart pounding, he dragged his gear out into the open and was soon over the fence and off along the river bank towards the town.

Gradually his composure returned and finding a shelter with a seat inside, thoughtfully provided by the council for the comfort of its citizens, he bedded down and tried to get back to sleep. It was obvious now why The Squatters rucksacks were all chewed away. They probably considered sleeping in a rat-infested wood yard as some kind of rite of passage but Terry vowed never to repeat the experience. The next morning, making his way back, he had to suffer mocking jeers from the rest as he displayed his gnawed rucksack, but the laughter was good-humoured and they soon turned to other topics.

A huge fire was blazing away and when it died down billy cans and army mess tins were produced and they fell to cooking breakfast. Terry and Hank had bacon and sausage carefully packed inside the snug fitting mess tins, and the rest were content with tins of whatever they had thieved the day before, Noddy being happy to eat cold beans straight from the tin. Last night's alcohol having had the usual dehydrating effect, the overwhelming desire was for tea and coffee, drunk black, with many spoonfuls of sugar. The sun broke through the clouds and they sat or lounged in various attitudes of ease, sipping from tin mugs, smoking woodbines, and contemplating the swirls and eddies of the muddy river. Hank threw a couple of dead branches on the fire and began cleaning his mess tins.

Sadly, this peaceful reverie was soon to be interrupted. Striding along the river bank towards the little group came a middle aged man, his face contorted with rage as he mouthed abuse in their direction. He was accompanied by a small wire-haired terrier happily barking along in chorus.

"What the hell di yi think ya doing lighting fires alang here yi bunch of louts?" he demanded. This indecorous and indiscreet approach had little or no effect on the assembled company, only Hank looked up from his cleaning job. The little dog had run on ahead and Hank gently reached out and allowed his hand to be sniffed before fondling its ears. By now the newcomer, dressed in corduroy and tweed, was standing over them airing his views on youth in general, and those who lit fires in particular. Hank stood up to face the stranger,

"Now then mate, nice dog you've got there" he said, ignoring the tirade, "you look like a military man to me". The military man's shoulders straightened imperceptibly and he answered proudly "Aye, Desert Rats". "Ah was in the mob meself" said Hank, "just national service like, saw a bit of action in Cyprus, nowt like you lads of course. Fancy a cup of tea?"

The old soldier looked down at the dirty faces, combat jackets and muddy boots, the billy cans on the fire and the tin mugs. His face softened.

"Aye, ahl have a cup wi yi lads" and he squatted down with practised ease. Soon he was regaling them with tales of war in the desert, how he had met Monty, even claiming to have seen Rommel through his field glasses. To Terry's surprise, Alex and Animal seemed well versed on the movements of the second world war and they chipped in with their own observations. The little dog, after exploring the camp and making the acquaintance of all the inhabitants, was finding the conversation less than riveting and began to tug at his master's trousers. Finally getting the message, he levered himself to his feet with the aid of his stick and set off to continue his walk. "Nice talking ti yi lads, don't forget ti douse that fire mind".

"Y'ill never know wiv been here" came Animal's reply.

In fact they never left any evidence of their presence, preferring to keep their bolt holes secret.

"How did you know he'd been in the army, Hank?" asked Terry. "Just a shot in the dark, kid", came the reply, "best to keep the natives friendly."

Jimmy Joe and Davey wheeled out their powerful bikes and kicked them into action. Pastel colours could be seen moving along the river bank and they purred off in search of talent. The rest set off towards the town still wearing their heavy coats seeming impervious to the warm morning sunshine.

Thanks to the 2is coffee bar in London, notional birthplace of British Rock 'n' Roll - where Tommy Steele and Cliff Richard were discovered - every small town now boasted a similar establishment, and Hexham was no exception. The local coffee bar had installed a juke box and sold cappuccino coffee. Girls were seldom to be seen unaccompanied in pubs, but were over represented in the local Bide a While or Toddle Inn. Terry soon found himself listening to the chat up lines of the ragged crew while Pat Boone's "April Love" simpered from the tinny juke box. Their unconventional appearance notwithstanding, they proved to be remarkably successful. Spud soon had his arm round a chubby young girl with a complexion little better than his own, but concealed by a liberal application of panstick. When her chubby hand disappeared inside the folds of Spud's duffel coat Terry averted his eyes. Eventually the two left together, Spud walking with an exaggerated stiff leg, and a filthy leer on his face to the accompaniment of ribald comments from the rest. To everyone's surprise Spud soon returned alone. "Wi bumped into ah parents on tha way ti church" he explained, removing his red bandanna, blowing his nose into it, then folding it neatly and knotting it back round his grubby throat. "Thi didn't seem ti take ti me, ah don't know why."

Animal was gazing out of the window with a distracted air when his attention focused on something disagreeable. "Wha not here, lads, it's the laughing policeman" he mouthed quietly before disappearing under the table. Terry peered out of the steamy window and did indeed see a fat and jolly red faced policeman - a sergeant in fact -accompanied by two constables. The trio strolled past, glanced briefly into the coffee bar and continued on their way, to the accompaniment of a communal sigh of relief from the boys. It transpired that this jolly looking chap was capable of sadism as vile as anything practised by the Spanish Inquisition. He knew the Squatters well and should he consider them to have caused him any inconvenience would wreak a terrible revenge. Whoever he could get his hands on, on whatever pretext, would be taken in for questioning before twelve noon on Sunday and released parched and cursing at the stroke of two p.m. closing time.

The panic over, Hexham Abbey clock struck twelve and they headed for the Royal Hotel. In the North East of England it is traditional to provide free cheese and biscuits on the bar on Sunday lunchtimes. Full advantage was taken of this practice and they moved from pub to pub filling up on the way. Apart from being thrown out of The Old Grey Bull because Alex and Animal took to eating the foliage of a tasty looking plant decorating the bar, the lunchtime passed peaceably. In the course of their perambulations Terry noticed several of the participants in last night's battle also doing the rounds. Nothing was said but he wondered whether there might be more trouble in the afternoon. As two-o'clock loomed, Terry's desire for beer was waning as fast as his money was running out. Now was the time to head for home. He left them just as things began to warm up, but he'd had enough excitement for one weekend.

"See you, Sunblest," shouted Hank. "W'll be in the Ould George the night if y' fancy it."

Leaving Home

Sunblest had other plans. He couldn't wait to get down to Simpson's Buffet to recount his adventures to Eric, Johnny and the rest of the crowd. A string of good lifts got him home in time to wash, change, borrow some money from his mother, bus into town and be bounding up the stairs of Simpson's Buffet by 8 o'clock. Mary was in attendance along with her assistant Florrie, a tiny woman with a large appetite for Brown Ale and Woodbines. A spot of good natured banter indulged in, 1/6d handed over, and soon Terry was headed down the long room as if walking down a Pullman carriage. At the last two tables sat the crowd bathed in the glow of the lamps looking like passengers on a crowded train.

Although the jazz club was in full swing the lads seemed to have abandoned it in favour of Simpson's which was fast becoming the headquarters of The Pagans. As soon as the opportunity presented itself Terry recounted his adventures with suitable embellishments. Eric who lived in Walker already knew Alex Baird, as his own home in Marondale Avenue was not far from Alex's in Scrogg Road. To the fertile imaginations of this crowd of bibliophiles the Squatters sounded like Danny and the boys from Steinbeck's "Cannery Row," crossed with the heroes of Kerouac's "On The Road". Perhaps someday soon they would try the life, but at the moment all their energy was concentrated on the band.

The fertile breeding ground of art school had thrown up another aspiring musician. Dave Ashcroft had succeeded in making his own instrument and was invited to join them on rhythm guitar. Ashie was in the company having his first rehearsal, which consisted of drinking pints and discussing repertoire. Chuck Berry songs predominated, followed closely by Gene Vincent, early Elvis, and a few Buddy Holly songs. Eddie Cochran and Fats Domino were also well represented. American rock & roll was the sole inspiration, the British variety being considered of little consequence. However, in the Autumn of 1958, Cliff Richard was to enter the charts at number 5, with his debut single "Move It", written by Ian Samwell of Cliff's backing group The Drifters. The lads considered this to be the greatest piece of British rock & roll ever, rivalling anything to come out of the States and it was immediately included in the play list. Sadly, Cliff was never to produce anything as good, turning - like his hero Elvis - to safe middle of the road material, achieving number 1 with the insipid "Living Doll" in August 1959.

The company that night included two more art students, Winston Scott and Phillip Payne. Phillip's main claim to fame was that he was having regular sex with his girl friend, what was more, in the comfort of a bed - something the rest of them had yet to achieve. He was always happy to discuss his sex life in loving detail, no doubt with the usual exaggerations. Contraception was a subject often discussed but rarely practised, and Phillip was considered something of an expert. He had discovered a spermicidal pessary with the wonderfully descriptive name of Ginamin which had to be inserted into the vagina ten minutes before sex took place. Terry pictured the scene. After rousing the girl into a state of sexual excitement came the delicate task of persuading her to insert a tablet the size of an Alka Seltzer into her vagina then indulging in small talk until it reached the required foaming consistency. All this while maintaining an erection that would not wilt at the prospect of being dipped into a pot of warm chemicals designed to kill sperm. However unromantic this may sound, in an age when fear of pregnancy was the greatest contraceptive of all, this alternative to condoms seemed to allay the girl's fears.

The talk turned from music and sex to literature, a subject close to his own heart. As with music the main inspiration came from America and John Steinbeck reigned supreme, followed by Kerouac and Salinger. They seemed to have dipped into most of the mainstream authors but were as happy to read the pulp fiction of Hal Ellison, writer of lurid tales featuring teenage gangs in New York. New Wave British authors also attracted attention, Saturday Night and Sunday Morning, Room At The Top, Lucky Jim, and John Wain's Hurry on Down, a copy of which resided in Dave Wilson's pocket at that very moment. Wilson, seeing Terry's interest handed over the severely mauled book with the promise of much more to come. Deeply engrossed in the book on the last bus home, Terry almost missed his stop.

In the weeks that followed, the Pagans' busy schedule of drinking, talking, playing the fool, and occasional practising turned them by some youthful magic into a great band. The next step was looking for gigs and they gradually began to appear at youth clubs, church halls and pubs. As usual the only transport was the bus and Terry often went along to lend a hand with the drums. This meant sleeping the night at Johnny's house, staying up late talking, listening to records and drinking beer. The Steel family without seeming to try, drew him into their friendly circle and made him feel relaxed and at home.

He especially enjoyed staying on the weekends when Johnny would cook the breakfast, walking into the enormous fridge - property of the Steels' wet fish shop adjoining the house - and taking out huge sausages and large brown eggs, he would then split the sausages down one side and place them in the heavy black frying pan that had never been washed in all its years of existence. Cooking gently in their own fat, the split sides curled out and allowed the inside of the sausage to turn a crisp dark brown. He then removed them and gently broke the eggs into the resultant fat, basting the deep yellow yolks gently until they too were done to perfection. Next the heat was turned up and thick slices of white bread quickly fried until golden, absorbing the last of the fat. All this, washed down with pints of sweet tea provided a feast laden down with masses of - as yet undiscovered - cholesterol.

If the band were not working on Saturday nights everyone met at the New Orleans Club. As the club did not open until 7-30 and officially stopped serving drinks at 10 o'clock it was considered essential to start early. 6 o'clock would find them in the nearby Tanners Arms filling up on Vaux Double Maxim and Sampson prior to queuing outside the club to be sure of a good seat. Included in this Saturday night tradition was an old school friend of Terry's named Bill Davidson and his girl friend Margaret Atkinson. Bill was often Terry's travelling companion on the last bus home and they shared an interest in jazz and blues. Bill was particularly interested in folk music. His father was a miner, one of the few who was determined that his own son should not go down "the pit". To this end he paid for his lad to attend a secretarial college in Newcastle where Bill was able to indulge in a great deal of screwing at an early age. However he eventually emerged with qualifications and secured a job in a solicitor's office. Now he was going steady with "a toony" as his grandmother would say and "no good would come of it". Terry had persuaded him to bring Margaret to the New Orleans to meet the crowd and it's pretty safe to say that their lives were never quite the same again. Bill himself would prove to be an important influence on future events. Margaret's brother Stan - yet another art student - began to turn out with them. A keen photographer, he unobtrusively captured the life and times of this little group of individualists carving out a life for themselves in post-war Britain.

Bottled beer was all that was available at this venue, mainly Brown Ale and its slightly weaker - and cheaper - companion, Amber. The Newcastle tradition of buying pint bottles and using a half pint glass meant that a lot of half empty bottles littered the tables at the end of the night. Such was their dislike of waste that the lads took to collecting the discarded beer and putting it to good use. An early example of conservation of resources or slopping, depending on your point of view.

If Terry was staying at Johnny's house they invariably took some beer back with them and Saturday nights often found the pair of them weaving their way along New Bridge street carrying a crate of Amber. Although Shieldfield was a rough district they walked through it cocooned in drunken innocence, adroitly avoiding the attentions of passing drunks with covetous eyes. The bus stop for Sheriff Hill was outside the Odeon cinema where they joined the courting couples - and more drunks - waiting for the bus to Gateshead. It is a tribute to their combined charm, wit, diplomacy, and occasional belligerence that they never lost a bottle.

It is well documented that the fifties was a time when youth was given its head but the parents of those kids were also enjoying the new affluence. A Labour government and socialist policies helped rebuild post-war Britain until - as often seems to be the case - people began to consider themselves well off enough to vote Tory. In January 1957 Harold Macmillan had won power leading a Conservative party far different from today's, their main pledge being to build 300,000 council houses, The age of Supermac had dawned and "we'd never had it so good". Adults who had lived through the hard times began to find themselves comparatively better off, and after indulging their children began to look for ways of brightening their own lives. No longer content to holiday at Blackpool or Skegness they began to look further afield. Billy Butlin was making his fortune opening holiday camps, but many turned their thoughts to foreign travel and the burgeoning package tour industry was eager to supply their needs.

For teenagers unwilling to join their parents on holiday and left in charge of the house, summer time was party time! Being in, or going around with, a band meant access to a larger selection of girls and invitations to more parties. The crowd preferred to be invited by posh tarts from Gosforth, or Jesmond. They felt no compunction in drinking the old man's whisky, pinching his golf clubs, or screwing his daughter. Another way of gaining admittance to a party was to gate-crash, purchase of a bottle of wine was useful on these occasions.

Wine drinking was an area of alcoholic consumption in which the crowd found themselves at a disadvantage, fortunately Newcastle Breweries provided the answer. One wine most people had heard of was the sickly concoction, Spanish Sauternes. The more salubrious hostelries, such as The Crows Nest, began to sell it to take away for the reasonable price of five shillings, just twice the price of a bottle of brown. Despite the colourful label it did not take long for someone to notice the wine was contained in Brown Ale bottles and from then on it was known as Brown Ale Sauternes, or for those determined to be coarse, Knicker-dropper!

Throughout the course of the summer of 1958, Eric, Jimmy, Blackie, Dave Wilson, George Stoves and many more were left in charge of their respective homes with dire warnings against any abuse of property. Terry found himself camping out in a variety of houses attending the inevitable parties, helping with the clearing up and crawling into work half dead. In the aftermath of a party the main casualties were crockery, carpets, and bed linen. Crockery could be replaced and carpets cleaned but the sheets posed a problem as operating some absent Mum's washing machine was neither feasible nor wise. The solution to the love letters written on the misused bedding came in the shape of the launderettes springing up on every high street and Terry spent a great deal of time reading books while the huge machines did the work, achieving a result far superior to the average twin tub.

Not having to rush off for the last bus was a luxury that very much appealed to Terry and living outside the constraints of parental pressure made him feel as free as his weekends in the country. He was now entering the fourth year of his apprenticeship, in receipt of a rise in wages, and working regular overtime. The idea of leaving home and finding a place of his own began to dominate his thoughts. Bringing the idea up in the forum of Simpson's won instant approval from the crowd, the idea of having somewhere to go midweek when you had no money for beer had a strong appeal. Dave Wilson confessed to finding his own home life a trifle suffocating. He had a desire for independence, self reliance, freedom to find his inner self, and plenty of late nights and screwing to help the process along .

They decided to get a place together, and two weeks later after much searching they presented themselves on the doorstep of a three storeyed Victorian terraced house overlooking the railway tracks in Heaton. Dressed in suits, and wearing ties, shoes shining and faces radiating innocence, two decent young men, a printer and a civil servant respectively, they soon persuaded the landlord that they would prove to be suitable tenants. To their delight the accommodation consisted of two attic rooms with a tiny kitchen adjoining, and a shared bathroom on the floor below. Living in a garret seemed a romantic notion, corresponding to their preconceived ideas of bedsit life.

To Terry, brought up in a tiny railway cottage with an outside toilet it seemed quite luxurious. The front room with a dormer window looking out over the railway tracks, was furnished with a three piece suite, table and chairs, and a reasonable carpet, a few nondescript prints hung on the walls. In the rear, illuminated only by a skylight was the bedroom with two single beds, a wardrobe and a chest of drawers. The landlord who lived on the ground floor was happy to let them move in at once, so they headed off to their respective homes to pick up their belongings.

As it was Saturday they were determined to be in residence that day. With all the arrogance and thoughtlessness of youth, Terry had hardly mentioned his plans to his widowed mother, or younger brother, and it was with some feelings of guilt that he returned home to pack his bag, and pick up his Dansette record player and record collection. His mother was remarkably sanguine, and his brother simply wished he was old enough to join him. So with promises of regular visits, he set off towards the bus stop with something of a lump in his throat, but freedom in his heart. Struggling on board the bus he spotted his regular travelling companion, Hazel, sitting alone. Glad to have someone to talk to, he threw himself into the seat next to her and began to regale her with his news. Over the last few months he had often seen her on the last bus waving her boyfriend goodbye. She would then sit with

Terry and hold his hand all the way home. He had watched her grow up and become more sophisticated in manner and dress. She had a good job in a building society and was up for promotion, now engaged to someone with excellent prospects and her future looked rosy. Yet somehow Terry could occasionally detect sadness clouding her lovely green eyes, just for a moment, then they would recapture their usual twinkle. When they parted at the Haymarket bus station she kissed him gently, and made him promise to ring her as soon as he was settled in and she would come straight from work and cook his tea.

That night Wilson and Terry were late in arriving at The New Orleans but soon caught up with the rest. They were already drunk with excitement. At the end of the evening, they set off across the Byker Bridge towards their new home, accompanied by Eric, Blackie, and Jimmie, and not a few bottles. After buying pease pudding and saveloy sandwiches at Headlam Street "dip shop" they walked down Heaton Road to Heaton Grove, and were soon tiptoeing up the stairs with much shushing and clinking of bottles. Not wishing to get off on the wrong foot, they kept the record player turned down and talked in hushed tones while putting paid to the saveloys. The three visitors were persuaded to leave early, and the new flat dwellers sat and drank the rest of the beer by the light of the gas fire, still too excited to go to sleep.

The next morning, having risen early, Terry strolled through the quiet Sunday morning streets of Heaton feeling wonderfully alive, a new chapter of his life was beginning and his senses tingled with heightened awareness. He looked towards the future with eager anticipation. Being anywhere near a shop that was open on Sunday morning seemed to him to be the height of sophistication and he bought the Sunday papers, bacon, eggs, butter, bread, a jar of coffee, and a bar of chocolate to eat on the way back. As he walked along tree-lined Heaton Grove the first train of the morning trundled past on its way to the coast. After cooking breakfast he raked a sleepy Wilson from his pit and they tucked in to the bacon and eggs, the sliced white bread and Lurpak butter on the table between them.

They were toying with the idea of washing up when the doorbell rang. Terry leaned out of the dormer window and saw Eric Burdon looking up at him from the tiny front garden. He suddenly remembered that they had arranged to go to the Felling Club near Johnny's place for the Sunday lunchtime session. Furnishing Eric with a cup of coffee while they washed and cleaned their teeth, they set off for Felling leaving the dishes to fester. Felling Club was the second home of Johnny's older brother, George, who would sign them in and validate their presence in a place where their offbeat appearance may have engendered some hostility. To lovers of good beer the club was paradise on Earth. They sold McEwans Scotch and the slightly stronger Special, both dark malty brews with thick creamy heads, so rich in fact that the bar was filled with row after row of half filled pints waiting to be topped up. They drank in the concert room, and on Sunday lunchtimes anyone could get up and sing, accompanied by Billy on piano, and Albert on drums. Eric usually got up and did a couple of numbers, sticking to old standards that most people would recognise such as "St Louis Blues", Johnny would take over from Albert and bang away on his basic kit of huge bass drum, hi-hat, and snare drum.

If they were lucky they would be invited back to George's or Johnny's for Sunday lunch. Both Steel households were geared to Sunday lunchtime drinking and the meal did not go on the table until three p.m. On this particular Sunday after six pints of special, Dave and Terry decided to exercise their new-found independence and cook their own dinner, forgetting in their drunkenness that there was little food in the house, so after more bacon and eggs they went back to bed, waking in time to go to the cinema.

Cinema-going was the most popular form of entertainment and Newcastle city centre managed to support six cinemas. The Haymarket, Odeon, Essoldo, Queens, Pavillion and Stoll, all did good business. Due to some strange quirk of the law cinemas were only licensed to open from Monday to Saturday. To open on Sundays needed a special licence and they were not allowed to show the current film on show that week. Consequently on Sunday nights one could choose from a menu of obscure old films, usually in black and white. As the audience consisted entirely of young people interested only in each other, the content of the film was of little interest and proved a perfect foil for the local wits to shout out ribald comments. Combing through the papers one occasionally unearthed an old classic such as "A Street Car Named Desire" but, classics or not, Sunday night was cinema night. At least it kept you out of the pubs so that you could get up for work on Mondays.

Terry and Dave found living together more difficult than they had imagined but they eventually got themselves into a routine of shopping, cooking, cleaning, and visiting the launderette. They were both confident that living in a flat would guarantee access to more than their fair share of sex and that they ought to be prepared for this eventuality. Apart from the dreaded Ginomin the only form of birth control was withdrawal, practised with little success by a frighteningly high proportion of youth, or condoms known mainly by the brand name of Durex, or colloquially as French Letters, Johnnies, or totally charmlessly, as blobs. The only place to buy these essentials to a worry-free life was at the barber's. As the average barber would consider Dave and Terry to be too young to be asked if they "needed anything for the weekend" and they were too embarrassed to broach the subject, another source of supply was needed. Fortunately Dave was more au fait with city life, and one Saturday lunchtime they set off for High Bridge in the heart of Newcastle.

After a couple of pints in The Duke of Wellington, Dave led the way to a tiny shop three doors away. The window display consisted of two small adverts for Durex on a background of chocolate brown and a great quantity of dust. Stepping inside they found themselves in a small square room with a counter running down the left hand side, devoid of either product or proprietor. They stood there uncertainly wondering whether to call "Shop", when a small man with slicked back hair, wearing rimless spectacles appeared as if from nowhere. He smiled an oily smile. "Can I help you" he asked.

"Two packets of Gossamer" said Dave without hesitation. When Terry's turn came he asked for two packets of Featherlite, not that he knew the difference, but just for the sake of sounding knowledgeable. Purchases complete they stepped back into the street with some relief. "A hope wi'll be seeing a lot more of that little bugger" said Terry.

"Aye, a hope two packets don't last us long", answered Dave more in hope than conviction.

Mission accomplished, they headed off up Grey Street towards Simpson's to seek out the rest of the crowd. In the weeks that followed, Jimmie, Blackie and Eric were frequent visitors to Heaton Grove, particularly Eric who would usually commandeer the settee on Saturday nights. A boy with a healthy appetite for sex, an interesting line in patter, and a great deal of perseverance, he usually managed to find someone to share the settee with him. Eric's girlfriends were usually long haired arty types, all beads, bangles, and ethnic dresses. They appeared to share a healthy attitude towards nudity, and Terry was treated to the sight of a large variety of breasts, from pert to pendulous, when he took in their coffee on Sunday mornings. His own sex life was not living up to his expectations and anxious for at very least some female companionship, he decided to take Hazel up on her offer of domesticity.

They arranged to meet at Grey's Monument straight from work, and proceeded to the Bigg Market to buy the ingredients for tea. On hearing of their arrangements Dave had tactfully decided it was time for him to visit his mother, so they had the flat to themselves. Hazel fell in love with the place and was soon busy in the tiny kitchen, while Terry searched through the record collection for something suitable to play, settling for a Lena Horne L.P.

A simple, but well cooked and tastefully presented meal of poached egg, mushrooms and baked beans was soon on the table, and it seemed to Terry to be pure ambrosia after his and Dave's efforts. This was followed by huge cream cakes that Hazel had insisted on buying and they giggled as the cream squirted out and had to be licked from sticky fingers. Terry sat back and studied his lovely companion dressed in her working clothes, the white blouse was still crisp and the dark blue pencil skirt virtually uncreased. She wore her dark red hair fashionably short and her red fingernails fashionably long. He did not usually care for long fingernails, or girls who smoked but he watched in fascination as she gracefully extracted a cigarette and he smelt the sulphur when the struck match burst into flame illuminating her red lips as she sucked the pale cylinder into life.

The times they had spent chatting on the last bus had formed a bond between them and they washed the dishes together talking and laughing like the old friends that they had become. Choosing two Frank Sinatra records and placing them on the stacking device on the record player, Terry took her into his arms and they danced slowly round the darkening room. It soon became obvious that Hazel had not just come for tea and soon their steps led them to the bedroom. Switching on the bedside light Terry turned to her. She reached out to him, her eyes smiling into his. He held her gently and kissed her soft yielding mouth, her darting tongue probed between his lips, the kiss seemed to go on forever and desire consumed his being. Trying not to fumble, he unloosened the buttons of her white blouse and slid his hands up her slim back, successfully dealing with the bra strap. Hazel had an aversion to sunbathing, her skin was white, almost translucent, accentuating the redness of her nipples.

By this time Terry was having difficulty controlling his passion and as he caressed her firm young breasts nature played him a dirty trick. Premature ejaculation was not a phrase in popular use, and certainly not part of Terry's vocabulary, but that was what had just occurred. Crestfallen and embarrassed he held her in his arms and whispered, "Ahm sorry Hazel, a got too excited, ahm sorry."

She prevented him from saying any more by kissing him full on the mouth. "Don't worry about it. I'm flattered, you must want me a lot.

Come on, let's get into bed."

With this, she removed the rest of her clothes, folding the blouse and skirt neatly and hanging them on the back of a chair, rolling down her filmy dark stockings with care and dropping the bra, suspender belt, and panties to the floor in one graceful movement.

Transfixed, he almost forgot to remove his own clothes as she stood before him naked for a few seconds before slipping into bed. Kicking his besmirched underpants beneath the bed, he climbed in beside her secure in the knowledge that a packet of featherlight nestled under the pillow. As she reached out her arms to receive him, all the sophistication and poise had receded and she looked vulnerable and unsure. "You do care for me Terry, don't you", she breathed.

His heart filled with tenderness. "Yes Hazel, I care, I care very much"

He gently kissed her eyes, cheeks, and mouth. This was the first time he had ever held a completely naked female body. He lay and luxuriated in the pleasure of it, breathing in the smell of her soft skin. They lay facing, gently stroking each other's bodies and he felt his passion return.

Soon they were making love. He successfully negotiated the condom without ruining the mood, and he felt her body relax beneath him. Her legs locked around his and her eyes rolled back in their sockets so that he could only see the whites and she began to moan softly. Although he had never heard or read the word orgasm, he had some vague idea that girls could "come" and knew that this was what he was about to experience. As the intensity increased and she thrust her pelvis against him he could hear a train approaching. Hazel's moans increased in volume, and she cried out loud as the train clattered past and they came together as the old house shook, and the windows rattled. "Right on time", laughed Terry, and they began to giggle, clinging together convulsed in joyous laughter until the tears ran down their faces. By the time their mirth had subsided, Terry imagined, the train would be pulling into Whitley Bay station

Hazel slipped next door, returning lighted cigarette in hand, comfortable with her nudity. He drank in the sight the dark red pubic hair livid against the white of her skin, proving if proof were needed, that red was her natural colour. He had never considered that watching someone smoke could be a sensual experience but so it was, and they chatted together until she had finished, then drifted off to sleep in each other's arms. When they awoke they made love again with less intensity and more tenderness. As they lay together Terry felt like the sanest man on earth. He cradled her head on his chest and gazed up at the skylight, reflecting that even the weather was on his side as he watched a cloud scud over a new moon.

His eyes traversed the sloping ceiling and came to rest on the alarm clock on the top of the wardrobe, placed there by Wilson in a desperate attempt to get himself out of bed on weekdays. It was ten p.m. He had twenty five minutes to get Hazel on the last bus home. Newcastle was blessed with regular trolley buses and he got her there on time, returning home to find Dave filling up the larder with tins of food provided by his anxious mum. Fishing around for a shilling, Terry fed the gas meter and lit the gas fire,. They sat in front of it and shared a bottle of Brown. He told Dave about the night's events but did not go into the details, feeling that it was too precious to share, or that he could not put his feelings into words. "You know, Dave", he said "she's engaged to this bloke and a think shi's gonna marry him, yet she wants to be with me, ah don't understand it".

Dave swirled the beer round in his glass and held it up to the light of the fire as if to inspect its clarity.

"Shi's a woman, man, that's the reason".

And with those profound words they finished off their beer and headed for bed.

During the weeks that followed Terry and Dave found that having a flat did indeed attract a lot of attention from the opposite sex and they found themselves making regular visits to the little shop on High Bridge.

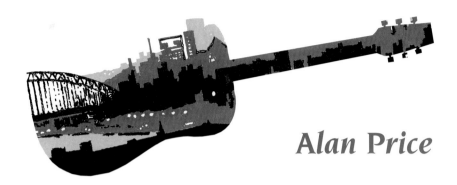

Alan Price

It was October 1958 and the music business was in the doldrums as far as rock and roll was concerned. Connie Francis was number one with "Stupid Cupid" when out of the blue came Cliff Richard in at number five with "Move It". Terry first heard the song at one of Chunkie Bourne's regular parties. Like most kids at that time Chunky's record player was a Dansette. If one swung out the arm that supported the records on the stacking device and put one record on the turntable it would play and replay the same record. "Move It" stayed on all night long. Was rock and roll enjoying a renaissance? No. By Christmas of that year, Conway Twitty was topping the charts with, "It's only make believe". February 1959 saw Shirley Bassey at the top and by March The Platters had dug up the old standard "Smoke Gets In Your Eyes". They may have been American, they may have been black, but it sure wasn't rock and roll.

The Pagans were scheduled to support the Frankie Hedley Combo at a church hall in Headlam Street, Byker, so as it was close to home Terry and Dave decided to go along. Although only fifteen minutes walk away Byker was a different world. When they walked south uphill towards Shields Road, Byker's main shopping street, they were walking away from the posh suburbs of Jesmond and Gosforth and towards the river, where the wealth of the city was generated. Headlam Street was one of the main arteries running from Shields Road down to the river Tyne, and was bisected by dozens of streets of identical terraced houses, which housed the workers on that busy waterway.

The people were hard working and insular, many of them rarely venturing across the Byker Bridge to Newcastle. The pubs were rough and the crowd never used them at weekends, but this was a Wednesday night, guaranteed to be pretty quiet. Terry still spent his lunch hours with George Stoves, who was spending a lot of time at Heaton Youth Club where Chas Chandler and Gordon Cleghorn often played as a duo doing mainly Everly Brothers songs. Terry invited George to the gig, and asked him to extend the invitation to Chas.

They had arranged to meet in The Raby Hotel on the corner of Shields Road and Raby Street, another main road leading down to the river. The Raby was reputed to be the hardest pub in Byker, but it was also known for the quality of its beer, so they decided to take a chance. When they entered the pub Chas and George were already there, feeding money into the juke box. The musical grapevine had been at work and they were soon joined by Chunkie Bourne and Alan Carr.

After a few pints they set off for Headlam Street buoyed up with drink and confident in the company of the bulky figures of Chas and Chunkie. Stepping into the church hall was like stepping back in time. Although a few of the boys were dressed like Chunkie and Chas in fashionable Italian style suits, the majority were still living in the Teddy Boy era, tasteless powder blue suits, string ties, and crepe-soled wedge-heeled shoes prevailed. Many of the girls wore hooped skirts guaranteed to expose suspendered thighs when they danced. Back-combed hair was the fashion and bouffants proliferated, along with pale lipstick, white high heels, and white handbags. But one didn't stare; their own ragged appearance was attracting enough attention.

The Pagans kicked off the evening with Jailhouse Rock followed by Twenty Flight Rock and Move It. As money was tight the band had no P.A. and Eric usually had to manage without a mike, relying on his powerful voice to carry the song. Frankie Hedley generously allowed them use of his equipment so with Eric's voice amplified Blackie, Jimmy and Ashie were able to turn up their own small amps and really rock the old church hall.

When the Frankie Hedley Combo took to the stage they proved to be a tight well-rehearsed band. Frankie took a professional approach to his music and was intent on making money out of it. He played piano and sang, performing a creditable rendition of Jerry Lee Lewis numbers with a sprinkling of Fats Domino songs thrown in. It was good honest rock and roll and, the boys had to admit, well performed.

Dave soon realised that he recognised the rhythm guitarist. A square jawed youth with a conventional haircut, he wore a grey suit and a sober tie. "Ah met that kid at a civil service do" said Dave, " I'm sure he told me he played piano"

Interval time arrived and they all strolled over to chat to the band. Dave homed in on the rhythm guitarist.

"Hello, it's Alan isn't it, Alan Price," said Dave. "Remember me?"

The youth was in the process of lighting a cigarette, and drew in a lung full of smoke before answering.

"How yi doing Dave? Yeah I remember. You were well pissed the last time ah saw you".

"Ay what a night" replied Dave, "Ah thought you told me you played piano?"

"I do", came the answer and as if to demonstrate he sat down on the piano stool. "But this band's already got a pianist."

He placed the cigarette between his lips and played a few exploratory chords, finally settling on "Honkey Tonk Train Blues" a Bill Doggett number from a few years earlier. Cigarette in his mouth and hair hanging in his eyes he pounded away at the badly tuned piano seeming oblivious to his rapidly gathering audience which consisted mainly of The Pagans and their friends. Eric and Johnny were particularly impressed, as much by his choice of song as his musical ability. Blues and boogie is what they would have preferred to play had there been an audience for it. Alan seemed heartened by the spontaneous round of applause that greeted him as he swung round on the piano stool, the remains of his cigarette now dangerously close to burning his lips.

The loquacious Burdon was soon deep in conversation with him, trading opinions on music and musicians and finally persuading Alan to sit in with The Pagans in the second half. He was conversant with some of the songs in their set such as "Ain't That a Shame " and "Let The Good Times Roll" and assured them he could vamp along with the rest. Much to Frankie Hedley's chagrin The Pagans - with no band uniform apart from matching county caps, and inferior equipment - were going down a storm. Not only that, they'd pinched his rhythm guitarist. Always a pragmatist, he realised he'd soon be looking for a substitute for Alan, and so it proved.

From that day on Alan Price abandoned regular well-paid work with Frankie, for irregular poorly paid work with The Pagans. But he would be playing piano and be part of a band which - had anyone ever thought about it - ran as a co-operative, and where his opinions mattered as much as anyone else.

Alan had dedicated so much of his time to playing piano that his social life was virtually non-existent. While other young men were out drinking and chasing woman, he was at home practising, determined to excel in his chosen instrument. Now he found himself with a complete new circle of friends who shared his love of music but didn't let it get in the way of having a good time.

The locals were all bopping away with a vengeance. Terry and Dave joined them and had no shortage of partners, but made no attempt to move in on any of the girls. This would have been a guaranteed way of inviting unwanted attention from the local yobs. There were two blonde girls dancing together who didn't quite fit the mould of a typical Byker girl. Terry and Dave split them up. Dave danced with the taller of the two, a leggy curvaceous creature with a superfluity of eye make-up who spoke with a pronounced lisp. Terry's partner was slim, bordering on skinny, with long hair and tasteful frugally applied make up. Both girls had masses of energy and danced with an abandon that suggested they'd consumed a fair quantity of alcohol. It transpired that they were fans of Frankie's band and had travelled up from Whitley Bay to see them.

On realising that they were not local, the two boys were soon in full chat-up mode. Dave's partner was Eileen and Terry's was Maureen. They both worked at a chemist's shop in Whitley Bay and had travelled up by train. Terry and Dave looked at each other. "Ah suppose yi got off at Heaton Grove" said Terry.

"Thaths right" lisped Eileen.

"We share a flat down there" Dave told them "just beside the station".

The minds of both boys were running through a variety of ploys to get the girls back to their place but they need not have bothered. "Thaths good", said Eileen "you can invite us back for supper, ah saw a "dip" shop up the road."

It seemed that she made all the decisions and did most of the talking, while Maureen seemed happy to acquiesce. They left the church hall while The Frankie Hedley Combo beat out "Great Balls of Fire" and were soon hurrying home with pease pudding and saveloy sandwiches swathed in newspaper to keep them hot. Taking care not to disturb the landlord they were soon in their attic abode, and while the girls oohed and aahed over the quaintness of it all, Dave selected the records while Terry put on the kettle. "Ahm sorry we've no drink in the house, girls" apologised Terry.

"That's all right" Maureen spoke up for once, "We don't need it", and both girls giggled, then proceeded to talk non-stop right through supper.

Once the food was gone and they were topping up on tea, Eileen began to fish round in her large white handbag, eventually producing a crumpled paper bag that looked as if it might contain sweets. "Doth anyone want one of these"? she asked opening the mouth of the bag and displaying the contents.

It contained what appeared to be Parma Violets.

"Tha purple heart'ths" she added before anyone could speak. "Drugth" she said triumphantly.

The boys' knowledge of drugs was purely anecdotal, they had read of 'goof balls' and such in American magazines and had seen Frank Sinatra's portrayal of a junkie in "The Man With The Golden Arm,'"but had no first hand experience. "What kind of drugs?" asked Dave. "Amphetamines" said Eileen, proudly displaying her pharmaceutical knowledge.

It was now clear why the girls had so much energy and so few inhibitions.

Always game to try something new Terry and Dave reached for the packet. "Where did you get them from?" enquired Terry holding an oval violet coloured tablet up to the light. "She pinched them from work" laughed Maureen, "she just walked into the pharmacy and scooped up a bag-full."

"Yah crackers man woman, y'ill get yourself sacked" said Terry, but Eileen was unconcerned and continued to hand out the tablets. "They take a while before they start working" she said, "but tha great".

Time was moving on and the girls made no mention of catching the train, Terry put on another record and turned off the main light. Nature took its course and in a very short time - modesty having been thrown to the winds - the springs of the two single beds were singing songs of love, or perhaps lust would be more accurate. The purple hearts seemed to heighten their awareness and certainly gave them more energy and it was in the early hours before they finally fell asleep.

Someone must have remembered to set the alarm as it went off on time. Terry awoke with a groan. His left arm had gone to sleep and Maureen still lay cradled in it. He looked down at the sleeping face. Mascara had run down her cheeks and a thin line of drool trickled from her mouth, but with blonde hair tumbling over her face she still looked beautiful. Gently removing his arm he headed for the bathroom, pausing only to put on the kettle. Soon they were all up and sitting round the table drinking tea, yawning and looking in very poor shape. "There is only one answer to this problem ", said Eileen, producing the crumpled sweet packet. "Another one of these."

From that time on, Eileen and Maureen were always around, and so were the purple hearts. Weekends were never quite the same again. Dave and Terry piled the girls onto the train for the coast and - keen for the crowd to try purple hearts - they arranged to see them in Simpsons on Friday.

When Friday finally rolled around they found they had a new drinking partner in the shape of Alan Price who turned up straight from work in the tax office, wearing his civil service suit and a white Mac. Alan lived in Jarrow and having worked late found it easier to eat in town then go straight to the pub rather than make the long journey to the coast and back. It soon became obvious that having a piano player in the band could create problems when it came to practising. They would need to find a pub with an empty back room and a piano. In the meantime Alan was invited to join them at The New Orleans the following evening where they could probably play the interval spot. If not, who cared? It would be a good night.

Although no one was aware of it at the time, Alan Price's introduction to the Pagans coincided with the release in America of a single by a black pianist named Ray Charles who was destined to have a profound influence on British popular music. "What'd I Say", based on the call and response of gospel music, reached number six in the American charts in the August of 1959. By some amazing feat of communal mental telepathy the whole crowd became aware of the record at about the same time. But it was Eric who tracked down and bought the single.

For no particular reason, other than that there had not been one for a while, a party was to be held at Johnny's house and "What'd I Say," parts one and two, both sides of the single dominated the record player. The addition of Alan Price and the influence of Ray Charles combined, contrived to lead the band in a new musical direction, away from rock and roll and towards big band blues.

This development did not appeal to Jimmy and Blackie who were rock and rollers at heart, and also had the ambition to make some money out of the music business. They began to look around for something else and eventually were offered places in a semi-pro. outfit called "The Gamblers", playing cover versions of chart numbers. The split was amicable enough and "The Gamblers" proved to be a good bunch of lads and soon became great friends with the Pagans crowd.

The Downbeat

Now, sad to say, it was the ex-Pagans. Little attempt was made to replace Jimmy and Blackie, and without the attraction of playing in the band, rhythm guitarist Dave Ashcroft drifted away from the crowd. So Eric, Johnny and Alan experienced something of a hiatus in their musical careers, but not in their social lives. There were still plenty of good times to be had. Some of which took place at The Corner House, a busy roadhouse at the Jesmond end of Heaton Road, within short walking distance of Terry and Dave's flat.

Monday night was jazz night in the pub's huge lounge and the band to feature there most frequently was an outfit called "The Mighty Joe Young Band" led by guitarist Joe Young. Joe liked to think of the band as the North East's answer to Eddie Condon. Guitarist Condon lead the legendary American band 'The Chicagoans' who had a reputation for unconventional behaviour and hard drinking so in that respect the comparison was fair. An enlightened bandleader Joe had a fairly eclectic taste in material and was happy to let Eric get up and sing the blues, something that the more purist trad bands refused to consider. Joe had recently taken on a new trumpeter, a Kings College student by the name of John Walters, John - now pretty much a household name - was destined to turn up again in the lives of Johnny, Eric, and Alan.

Running on Tuesday nights was the inappropriately named Ballads and Blues club, probably one of the first folk clubs in the country. The venue was The Barras Bridge Hotel, situated near where the Civic Centre now stands, one of the many pubs to fall victim to the wrecking ball during Newcastle's spate of "modernisation" in the sixties. The Skiffle boom with its speeded up versions of American folk songs sparked off an interest in British folk music inspiring a dedicated few to research their own musical heritage.

Among these was Johnny Handle who Terry remembered having seen at The Newcastle Jazz Club playing trumpet and piano at the same time, a performance that made up in exuberance what it lacked in skill. Now Johnny was playing guitar and singing such traditional North East songs as "The Dirty Black Legged Miner" and, along with the likes of Louis Killen was carving out a place for "Geordie" folk music that still thrives today. Tuesday nights at the Barras Bridge soon became part of the week's itinerary and although Eric and Alan never performed, they certainly absorbed the musical influences.

No one ever seemed to want to spend an evening at home in front of the television, now a dominant intruder into most homes. So long as they could scrape some money together the crowd were out on the town. Wednesday was a quiet night, so someone suggested a visit to the Theatre Royal on Grey Street, an imposing building in an elegant street. If you were prepared to sit in "the gods" almost scraping the ceiling, it made for a cheap night. Of course there was a bar and the boys bought bottles of Guinness from a tiny old lady of about eighty who wore a black dress with a starched white collar and could never get the change right.

They became regular Wednesday night theatregoers, and sandwiched in between the usual diet of murder mysteries, musicals, and revues, they thrilled to some of the great drama produced by the new wave of young playwrights. John Osborne's "Look Back In Anger" was the first to impress them and they went on to see plays by the likes of Pinter, Wesker, and Delaney, all new to their uncultured, but uncluttered young minds.

Lack of money usually meant an enforced Thursday night in, ready for Friday, pay day and everyone's big night out. They usually spent Friday nights in Simpsons or in a tiny pub called the Grape Vaults situated near Grey's Monument. The Grapes sold Newcastle Exhibition the quality of which would bring tears to the eyes of any lover of beer, and they would sit round the brass topped tables in the tiny back room drinking halves of Ex., enjoying waiter service and thinking themselves in paradise.

Friday nights were soon to change. Mike Jeffries of Nelson Street fame was in the process of opening a new club in a disused warehouse off Carliol Square. An art college friend of Eric's by the name of Joe Pharoe was commissioned to design the interior and everyone was agog to know the details. Because of his stature - he was less than five foot tall - Joe was known as "little Joe," or because of his surname he was called Tut after the Pharoah Tutankahmun. He took to appearing at The Grapes, usually spattered with black and white paint to sink a few halves and let them know how things were going. First he had painted the whole club black, then painted a series of murals on the walls in white, hardly revolutionary by today's standards but considered very avant-garde at the time. As Tut was a big Steinbeck fan the murals consisted of scenes from his books, mainly Cannery Row and Tortilla Flat. As Jeffries was not paying Tut a great deal of money and had little idea of how the club should look he was given full licence to indulge his fantasies, and if the result was not to everyone's taste it was certainly different.

Opening night finally arrived and the crowd were out in force, this club was something different. Nelson Street had a dance floor but no bar, the New Orleans had a bar but no dance floor, and neither had a late licence. Here was a club with a late bar and dance floor in a suitably sleazy part of town with decor by one of their own. "The Downbeat" became the high spot of the week.

82

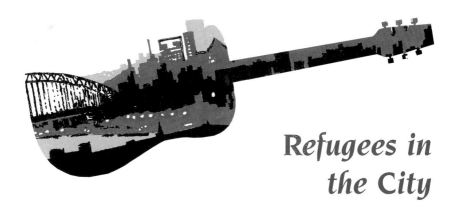

Refugees in the City

If Alan Price considered himself to have fallen in with a pretty lively crowd, he was about to have an experience that would test his stamina and tolerance to the limit. 1959 was World Refugee Year and in an effort to illustrate the desperate plight and living conditions of refugees around the world a mini shanty town had been built on the lawn in front of The Laing Art Gallery on New Bridge Street. In an effort to raise funds a group of King's College students intended to sleep in these huts and issued a challenge to anyone prepared to do the same. Who should pick up this gauntlet but Eric Burdon, and who would accompany him? All his mates, easily persuaded after several pints in Simpsons.

So it came to pass that Terry, Dave, Eric, Alan, George Stoves, Winston Scott and Philip Payne set up camp in the middle of the city, much to the amazement of its citizens. Collecting boxes had been provided so they immediately began panhandling the passing populace with reasonable success. As the rush hour crowds began to dwindle boredom set in. Eric gazed along the street to the huge clock on Cooks corner, a popular meeting place for courting couples. "Hey lads, the pubs are open" he said with a grin, "anyone fancy a pint?"

The King's College lot had not yet put on an appearance, so off they trooped to Simpson's. One pint led to another and time flew, as time will in the convivial atmosphere of a public house until eventually Mary threw them out into the cheerless environs of Nelson Street which, because of its close proximity to the green market, smelled like Mott Street in New York, but no one had written a song about it. A belly full of beer and the cold night air brought on pangs of hunger.

With one accord they set off towards the Central Station, tucked away on the outskirts of which was the Railway Canteen. This establishment had been built to provide hot food for railway employees at any time of the day or night. No doubt the occasional train driver used it during the day, but at night the customers were the people of the night. The whores, drunks, criminals, tramps and general dross that gravitates towards the dirty corners of any city eventually found their way there, to while away as much of the night as possible without attracting the attention of the railway police.

So, on the first night of their privations they crawled into sleeping bags in the squalid huts having spent enough on beer alone to feed the average refugee for a week. In the course of the next two weeks, Terry was to sample the ale in almost every pub in Newcastle, the wares of most of the sleazy cafes, and become familiar with the inside of all the public toilets.

Terry, George, Alan and Dave were going to work every day and the rest were attending art college. It was particularly difficult for Alan Price as he worked in the tax office dealing with the public and was expected to look neat and tidy at all times. He took to going in to work early, washing and shaving in the toilets, rubbing out the collar of his spare white shirt and leaving it to dry in a storage cupboard. Dave, also a civil servant, had similar problems. Of the others, some of them did not shave yet and the rest did not bother, but managed to keep themselves reasonably clean.

It soon became clear that they could not maintain this pace of life for long without a fresh injection of capital. They began to eye the collection boxes with interest. Every night Hadaway, the student who had issued the challenge, took the boxes and handed them over to the nearby city library for safe keeping. Phillip managed to "liberate" one of the boxes and having participated in several college "rag weeks", soon managed to open it up. Reasoning that no money would be collected at all without their participation, they decided that this box would furnish them with expenses.

Once the newspapers got wind of their "praiseworthy efforts" they became something of a cause celebre in the town and the takings went up. The pubs closed at ten and the last buses were heading out of town around eleven. This meant that when they staggered out of the railway canteen after twelve they were walking through a city eerily devoid of people and with only the occasional car cruising past. This was the time they loved best, feeling at one with the soot-stained old buildings, as they strolled along Collingwood Street and up Grey Street, their voices echoing across the broad thoroughfare disturbing the starlings nesting on the many ledges on the elegant facades. Of course they were constantly stopped by the police but once having explained their status as youthful ambassadors for world refugees they were allowed to proceed unmolested.

Alan, who usually practised every night was missing his piano. So they decided to look round for a pub that had not yet succumbed to the culture of the juke box and possessed a piano that was reasonably in tune. They settled on the Cumberland Arms opposite the Empire Theatre on Percy Street. This was a place often frequented by Chas Chandler and his mates. Unfortunately they were not there on this particular occasion when their hefty presence would have been useful. After a couple of pints Alan settled himself on the piano stool and opened up with "What A Friend We Have In Jesus" a song he remembered from his Methodist childhood. Having warmed up his fingers he suddenly burst into Little Richard's "Good Golly Miss Molly" and was joined on vocals by Eric. This was followed by Jerry Lee's "High School Confidential", and the rest of them joined in. Soon the joint was rocking, to paraphrase the lyrics of the next song, "Reeling and Rocking" by

Chuck Berry.

By now everyone in the bar was taking notice, including a bunch of youths whose attentions would prove unwelcome. There were five of them, and they elbowed their way through to the piano and began making inane offensive remarks calculated to demoralise the pianist. Alan wisely kept his head down and kept on playing. Terry recognised the type. They were the kind of animals that run in packs, there would be no reasoning with them, they just wanted to beat someone up, and this load of soft looking clever shites would do.

On entering the pub Terry had noticed a couple of body builders from his home village propping up the bar. Joss Wheatly and Marty Wells were huge specimens, the first people to be seen wandering round the streets of Newcastle wearing only jeans and tee shirts in midwinter. Thinking on his feet he made his way over to them. "Hya Joss, Marty remember me? Ahm one of Davey Tunnah's mates."

"Aye, a remember yi kid" replied Joss- who was a friendly soul - "how yi doing?" "Ah think we've got whaselves into a bit of bother over there" Terry replied dispensing with the niceties "do you mind if ah use your name?"

"Yi can use my name, kid, but ahm not fighting yah battles for yi" said Joss, and Marty grunted in agreement.

Terry headed straight back to the crowd where things were beginning to turn nasty. His heart was beating fast but he tried to appear relaxed as he stepped up to the obvious leader of the group. "Look, I don't know whether you realise, but that pianist is in Billy Fury's backing band (Billy Fury was playing The Empire that week) and those two are Billy's minders, they are Americans, probably in the Mafia or something."

He waved over to Marty and Joss who obligingly waved back. The scrawny leader looked unsure and while his pimply brow was knitted in thought, Terry took his chance. "Come on Alan, you'd better get back to the theatre, you'll be on soon."

Alan did not hesitate. Slamming down the piano lid, he stood up and made for the door trying to look as unhurried as possible. The rest followed suit, endeavouring to melt away rather than make a run for it. Terry was the last to leave, pausing only to have a quick word with his two would-be protectors for the sake of authenticity.

Once outside, without consulting each other they disappeared up the first back lane they came to and kept moving until they judged themselves to be far enough away from The Cumberland to feel safe. "We should have fought the bastards" said Phillip Payne "there's more of us than there are of them". "You've got to be joking" answered Eric, "you don't fight vicious bastards like that, even if you won they'd only get their mates and hunt you down. No ah think this is one occasion when discretion is the better part of valour".

"Once thi realise those two buggars arc not American Mafia thill be on wha trail anyway" laughed Terry.

"Ah reckon wi need some back up, let's go down the Old George and see if The Squatters are there."

So they headed down the Cloth Market slipped into the bar of the George and were relieved to find Big Alex, Animal Hogg and Hank sitting near the fire, having a quiet drink. Terry made the introductions and recounted the tale of their recent encounter which made little impression. Alex changed the topic to music and was soon airing his considerable knowledge of jazz and blues much to the surprise of the whole crowd and Alan Price in particular. This led Terry to believe that he might after all be able to persuade them to join the Squatters on one of their weekend sorties into the countryside. After all it could hardly be worse than the conditions they were enduring at the moment.

After eight days the King's College students admitted defeat and threw in the towel. The crowd decided to stick it out for a few more days. By now they were all looking decidedly the worse for wear. Their clothing was filthy and they had sustained a great many cuts and bruises while indulging in their new hobby of tearing down the huge posters and advertising hoardings to line the walls of their huts. Various street signs also began to appear on the walls, along with Keep Off The Grass, Post No Bills, and information regarding the whereabouts of the nearest clinic for venereal disease. They took to scouring the building sites for wood, lighting a huge fire every night and singing round it until the early hours.

The police decided that the novelty was wearing off, stern warnings were issued and their freedom to roam began to be curtailed. At the end of almost two weeks, Winston had suffered a broken wrist while indulging in a bit of scaffold climbing, Phillip was in hospital with pleurisy and alcoholic poisoning, while the rest were suffering from a variety of bowel disorders and exhaustion. It was time to call it a day.

Whether the refugees of the world derived any benefit from their efforts is doubtful but on a personal level it certainly made them appreciate their own warm homes and secure lives, while making them aware that their internal organs were not indestructible.

They returned to the usual round of clubs and pubs and after a few weeks, sensing that boredom was beginning to set in, Terry suggested a weekend away with The Squatters. Everyone agreed, including Alan Price who, by some unspoken agreement, was now referred to as Pricey.

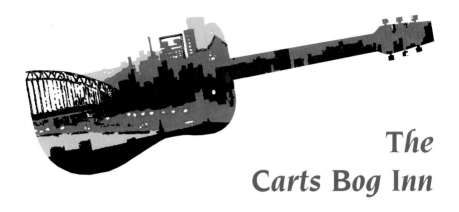

The
Carts Bog Inn

A visit to the Old George by Eric and Terry elicited the information that the weekend's destination was to be Starward Gorge near Alandale. Big Alex being a lover of music could see the advantage of including a piano player in the party and assured them that the Carts Bog Inn, the pub they would be using, had a good piano.

As Pricey had no experience of hitchhiking, Terry volunteered to show him the ropes, so Saturday morning found them heading off up the West road out of Newcastle towards Hexham, Alan sporting a brand new wind-cheater and carrying a borrowed rucksack firmly on both shoulders. (The style among the Squatters was to hang the 'ruck' casually from one shoulder). He was a little nervous at first but after a few short lifts he relaxed and was soon enthusing about this new, exciting and cheap way of seeing the world.

They sailed into Hexham on the back of a brewery dray and dismounted in front of the Royal Hotel hitting the pavement before the lorry shuddered to a halt and, with a wave of thanks to the driver, they headed for the bus station. Eric and Johnny were already there along with Alex, Animal, Hank, Spud, Geronimo, Red, and Noddy. Terry recognised four Gateshead lasses who sometimes joined the crowd. Jean, Paula, Irene and Thelma were kitted out with boots and rucksacks and looked as hard as any of the lads, and a lot harder than Pricey. Hank and Noddy occupied themselves

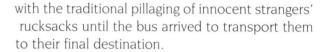

with the traditional pillaging of innocent strangers' rucksacks until the bus arrived to transport them to their final destination.

The Carts Bog Inn was, and is, part of a farm and is owned and run by the farmer to subsidise his agricultural activities. At that time it consisted of two small rough-plastered rooms, each with a huge fireplace. The furniture consisted of a miscellany of shabby mismatched items sturdy enough to withstand the depredations of farmhands and hikers. The larger back room which served as the bar contained one prize item of furniture. A beautiful upright piano with walnut inlay and brass candlesticks.

Alex and Animal bellied up to the bar exuding menace and mischief in equal proportions. The landlord, a huge sandy-haired man with the ruddy complexion of a typical farmer was unperturbed." Ahl serve yi Alex as long as you promise ti behave yaself".

"Us behave wahselves" roared Animal with a grin, "why, we are gentlemen, knights of the road, defenders of the poor, rescuers of damsels in distress."

He would have continued in this vein for sometime but the landlord intervened. "Shut up, Animal, for crissake, what are you drinking?"

Soon they had all been served, and Pricey having tried the piano lid and found it locked was leafing through the sheet music in the piano stool. Spud took the initiative,

"Di yi mind if wha mate has a go on your piano, Simon?" he said, addressing the man behind the bar in what he considered to be a charming manner. "No chance" came the abrupt reply, "that's my son's piano and nobody plays it but him".

"He'll not harm it" chimed in Noddy with a deprecating leer. "He plays in church".

"Chapel actually" said Pricey. " I can play, and I have a great deal of respect for pianos".

Eventually Simon relented, produced a key and uttering dire threats on the consequences of any damage, opened the piano lid. Alan put the landlord's mind at rest by warming up with "What a friend we have in Jesus", a song he had indeed learned in chapel, continuing with some current favourites in quiet mode such as "Its Only Make Believe" by Conway Twitty, and The Platters version of "Smoke Gets in Your Eyes". Johnny produced

Photo call outside Hexham Abbey

a pair of brushes from his inside pocket and kept the rhythm on an upturned beer tray. Eric who possessed an uncanny memory for song lyrics sang along, with tentative back-up from Terry.

The Squatters affected not to be impressed by this demonstration of musical virtuosity, but the girls moved to a table near the piano and watched Alan's hands with rapt attention. Jean and Paula proved to be good on song lyrics and as the beer went down all shyness vanished and they were soon singing along with gusto, Irene and Thelma joining in where they could. The landlord beamed benignly as he served up pints and listened to the music of the cash register. Pricey had obviously decided to warm things up and when Terry heard him playing the opening chords of the Jerry Lee Lewis rocker "High School Confidential" he stepped in quickly. "Not just now Alan. Wiv got the night to think about, thas no more pubs around here."

Getting the message he eased into "Honkey Tonk Train Blues" which caused a great deal of foot stamping and table bashing but no outright riotous behaviour.

Three o-clock, afternoon closing time, arrived without incident and the landlord hurried them out, anxious to get on with his farming chores. They had not travelled far across the fields towards Starward Gorge when they became aware of the voice of farmer Simon calling them back. Christ, thought Terry, one of this lot's been up to mischief, but it was not so.

"Lads a need yah help" called out the perspiring farmer. "One of me calves is stuck in a culvert, if ah divnt get it oot soon it's liable to die of a heart attack."

They dutifully trooped back to the edge of the field where a drainage pipe ran under the road. The wretched animal's cries, amplified by the pipe, made a mournful sound.

"Yi need somebody slim ti get in there and push it out," said Red eyeing the skinny figure of Geronimo meaningfully.

Geronimo, swathed in black leather with slicked-back hair that looked to be made out of the same material, sneered his Elvis Presley sneer. "Find another mug, am nee country boy".

"Yih might not be a country boy but yar a cunt" said Red advancing on the defiant figure. "Ahll give yi a hand in" he said, grinning a demonic grin.

Before Geronimo could react Spud spoke up. "Nee sweat lads, ahll dee it."

The filthy duffel coat was deposited on the grass, followed by a tattered checked shirt and there stood Spud in jeans, boots, and neckerchief his skinny acne-covered body exposed to the afternoon sun. He disappeared into the culvert on his hands and knees muttering soothing words to the frantic animal, while the anxious farmer crossed the road to await its rebirth into the world. After much cursing, pushing and straining on the part of the valiant Spud, the calf was finally delivered into its owner's arms seeming no worse for its experience. Then Spud appeared, grinning triumphantly and covered from head to foot in shit. The assembled company dissolved into helpless laughter as he pirouetted before them in all his steaming glory. The grateful farmer took him to the farm yard and hosed him down while apologising for his calf's incontinence and promising free pints that evening.

After this entertaining diversion they set off for the woods and were soon gazing down into a beautiful valley carved out by the upper reaches of the river Tyne, home to a wide variety of broadleaf trees and a great many pines. Seeking out a clearing near the river they sprawled out in the sun, listened to the soothing sound of the babbling water and breathed in the clean country air.

Pretty soon the country air was being polluted by cigarette smoke and the silence shattered by the sound of Red snapping off a rotten limb from an old oak tree. So remote was this lonely place that there was an abundance of forest debris suitable for burning and the rest followed his example and quickly accumulated a huge pile of wood ready for the inevitable bonfire to be lit that evening. Hank built a small fire for the immediate business of cooking, while Noddy went through the spoils from their recent depredations of the hikers' rucksacks. "What's ahll this?" he cursed . "Thas tins of pineapples, beans, and all kinds, but nee meat."

He began to heap imprecations on the shoulders of all hikers and their mothers who had deprived him of sustenance, managing to entertain everyone in the process.

While this diatribe was taking place it occurred to Terry that he might well be able to raise his own esteem in the eyes of the Squatters. Raised on the outskirts of a pit village in Northumberland he had been shown by an old miner turned poacher how to kill a rabbit with a steel ball-bearing fired from a catapult. Nostalgia for his childhood had recently prompted him to purchase a factory made steel catapult - something he could never have afforded in his childhood. "Yi fancy gannin after some rabbits Geron?" enquired Terry.

"Aye, why not?" said the youth grinding his fag into the dust, "nowt doing here."

As they strode off into the woods together, Geronimo changed from a pseudo Elvis Presley to a stealthy alert Indian brave, a persona more suited to the real boy.

As the noise of the camp faded into the distance, they slowed their pace, stepping silently and cautiously, their senses alive to the ambience of the forest. Eventually they came upon the dappled shade of a glade where several rabbits could be seen nibbling at the lush grass. Terry produced his catapult and to Geronimo's surprise and his own amazement killed a rabbit with his first shot. "That's the last yill see of them buggers" said Geronimo as he picked up the rabbit by the back legs.

"Nah," replied Terry "rabbits have got short memories."

Sure enough the conies soon returned and after a few missed shots, they managed to kill two more.

They returned to the camp in triumph. "Anybody here know how to skin a rabbit?" shouted Terry.

"Aye, we can" affirmed Noddy. "Me and Hank have done a few in wha time", he said with a conspiratorial smirk.

"That's right" Hank agreed, "but most of them were cats. Tha was a meat shortage after the war and the local butcher wasn't too particular. Ah had aboot a dozen in the coalhoose once ready for the chop when me mother went for some coal. Shi nearly shit aself tha was cats ahll ower the yard".

"Didn't yi get a belt off yah dad?" asked Terry in innocent wonder.

"That bastard never came back from the war" snarled Hank.

"Killed in action?" asked Jean.

Hank laughed. "He got himself wounded, convalesced in Rome and shacked up with some Iytie tart. Ah suppose ah divn't blame im, it's got to be better than Gateshead."

Casting such thoughts aside he produced a hunting knife and set about the first rabbit. With Noddie's help he soon had them skinned, skewered and roasting over the fire. Bread and beans were produced and the meal commenced, though the girls demurred, preferring to stick to their own tinned food. The repast was soon devoured, dishes washed in the river, tins buried, and rabbit skins cast into the undergrowth.

To Terry's chagrin no mention was made of his skill as a hunter, but what did he expect? The boys lay round the fire grimy and replete, while the girls saw to their make-up. Red began to damp down the fire. "The pubs are nearly open", he roared, "Ahm thirsty."

Red suffered from a slight limp, the result of some escapade in his interesting past and had taken to carrying a huge staff to help him over any difficult terrain. He stomped off up the valley, red hair unkempt and long coat billowing out behind him. Animal and Alex fell in beside him, with Hank, Noddy, Geronimo, and Spud bringing up the rear. They reached the crest of the hill, and silhouetted against the sky, looked, to Terry's romantic eye, like a bunch of border reivers setting out on a raid. Eric, Johnny, Pricey, and Terry, accompanied the girls with Pricey showing particular interest in Thelma, whose sturdy frame needed no help from any boy.

When they reached the inn, the vanguard were already sitting behind foaming pints indulging in beer talk with all the reverence of wine snobs. After a couple of pints, Pricey seated himself at the piano and played a couple of slow blues, then moved on up into some boogie-woogie, then it was "High School Confidential", and "Rocking at the High School Hop", became "Rocking at The Carts Bog Inn." Johnny had brought along his drumsticks, and in the afternoon he had noticed a small leather suitcase containing sheet music next to the piano. Having read that Crickets' drummer Jerry Allison had employed a suitcase to create a new sound on the song "I'm Gonna Love You Too", he'd decided this was the time to try it out and was soon laying down a solid beat on the ancient leather. Taking that as a cue Eric took to the floor and launched into "Think It Over", another Buddy Holly song. From then on it was rock and roll all the way and the tiny room reverberated to a music as yet unheard in that isolated spot.

Still grateful for the rescue of his calf, the landlord made no complaint. Most of the bemused locals had chosen to sit in the other room and Simon joined them, only putting in an appearance when someone called for beer, which was often. A steady stream of pints appeared on top of the piano and the young artistes obligingly drank them with a little help from Terry. As is usual, the girls were the first up to dance but eventually everyone was on their feet, including the usually recalcitrant Hank who only sat down when he realised that valuable drinking time was being wasted.

Soon it was dancing-on-the-tables time, and things were beginning to get out of hand when Simon began to call time.

Such were the archaic licensing laws that in theory a landlord could sell a person a drink at one minute to ten and take it off him at one minute past. What in fact happened was that those greedy for more ordered as much as possible before time, and spent as long as possible drinking it while being harassed by the landlord. Eventually all glasses were emptied, carry-outs bought, and the peace and quiet was shattered as they made their boisterous way across the fields.

So far north were they that the summer evening was still light and Alan Price, the only one with a watch, took occasion to glance at his timepiece. " Lads, it's only quarter past nine", he shouted.

"The bastard", roared Animal, "wiv been conned."

The effect was instant, the whole contingent wheeled round and ran back across the fields, uttering oaths and heaping abuse on the head of the landlord.

When they arrived at the inn Simon was waiting at the door grinning broadly. "Well it was worth a try, wi wah only trying to get a bit of peace and quiet at the end of the night. These lads have got to get up early in the morning" he said, indicating the various agricultural types now propping up the bar.

His grin was infectious and the crowd used up what little breath they had left laughing at their own expense. A few more carry-outs later they set off back across the fields.

As they reached the lip of the valley, flames could be seen reflected in the sheen of the dark river. Ever practical, Hank, realising the futility of going back, had carried on and ignited the waiting bonfire. The sight of the flames spurred them on and they were soon basking in the fire's warmth. Alex and Animal proceeded to pile on more logs creating an incandescent ball of light and heat to drive away the encroaching darkness. Bottles were opened, cigarettes lit and sleeping bags rolled out for comfort on the forest floor.

Jean seemed to naturally gravitate towards Big Alex, and she was soon seated next to him her head nestled against his huge chest. Eric, Johnny and Pricey sat and chatted to the rest of the girls while Terry and Geronimo went off in search of firewood, more for the excitement of moving among the huge trees in the flickering firelight than any real need. After consuming more alcohol the wilder element decided that the night was not yet over, so Animal, Hank, Red, Spud, and Noddy took to leaping through the flames daring each other to jump closer to the centre of the greedy inferno. The inevitable happened and Spud headed for the river, his clothes in flames. He returned wet, singed and grinning. "Yi nearly had meat for supper" he quipped, cracking open another bottle, utilising his yellow teeth to remove the crown cork.

He stood before the fire steaming gently, somehow signifying that things should quieten down.

Thelma sat alone, firelight accentuating the highlights in her black shoulder-length hair, dark eyes reflecting the flames. Her face, hardened by life in the slums of Gateshead, had softened in the glow and allowed her true beauty to shine through. Pricey sauntered over to her and soon they were swapping anecdotes and cigarettes. Terry grinned wryly to himself when he noticed that the ever randy Eric had taken Irene to one side and was engaging in a pretty one-sided conversation. However it must have been a good line of patter, for her head nodded in agreement causing blonde curls to tumble round her face in an appealing fashion.

People began to crawl into their respective sleeping bags, moving as close to the fire as was practicable, while Alex piled on a few extra logs. Paula appeared from some unspecified errand beyond the circle of the flames and sat down next to Terry. "Haway Sunblest, give us a song", she said taking his hand in hers.

"Ah cannat sing, man" he protested, but with a little more coaxing the two of them were soon dueting "That Old Black Magic".

They ran through a few more romantic ballads until they had exhausted their repertoire and themselves.

Terry yawned, "Ah wonder if your sleeping bag will zip together with mine" he asked, trying his best to sound casual.

"Wi'll soon find out" came the reply, and suiting her actions to her words began zipping the two together. Lo and behold, they fitted.

"Well there's a thing" she smiled removing her boots and duffle coat and climbing in.

"Aye, fancy that" said Terry doing the same.

Not that he had any illusions about his chances of a sexual conquest; he knew Paula well enough not to make that assumption. After a protracted and amorous goodnight they drifted off to sleep in each other's arms, as the fire died down to a glimmer of intermittent light.

After a dreamless sleep, the gradual dawning of a new morning began to penetrate Terry's eyelids and he slowly opened his eyes. Although he had slept through the clamour of the morning chorus there was still plenty of birdsong filling the air, and an abundance of small birds picking over the debris of the previous day. The pain of his full bladder was only out-weighed by the throbbing of his temples, and his morning erection threatened the stitching of his jeans.

Crawling painfully from the sleeping bag he hobbled off towards the river. Resting his brow against the cool mossy bark of an oak tree he proceeded to water its gnarled old roots. So involved was he in the ecstasy of relief, that he had not noticed Pricey sitting on a fallen tree a few yards away. Zipping up his fly, he became aware of his presence and made his way to the disconsolate figure who was fiercely smoking a cigarette as if he owed it a grudge. "Morning Alan, you don't look too happy".

"Aye, well ah thought it would of been my night last night with that

Thelma", came the reply.

"Pricey man, ah could of told you yah never ganna screw one of these lasses" said Terry.

"Thiv got more sense than ti get knocked up by some bloke thiv never met, and might never see again. You take Thelma out a few times, show her a bit of commitment and when shi's ready, she'll have you."

Pricey threw the cigarette in the general direction of the river. "Maybe you're right, maybe ah learned something last night."

"Anyway" said Terry cheerfully, "they're still nice to sleep with, let's get that fire stoked up, ahm ganna make Paula a cup of coffee, then ahm getting back in with her."

Within the next hour everyone had surfaced and they spent the rest

Jean Reay & Animal Hogg

of the day exploring the delights of Starward Gorge, climbing trees, swimming in the river, swinging on tree swings and generally reliving their childhood, although most of them had experienced growing up in far less idyllic surroundings.

Johnny, Eric and Pricey were keen to make the Nelson Street Jazz Club that night so decided to set off back. After hesitating for some time over Paula, Terry joined them and soon they were back on the main road at the bus stop with little idea whether a bus was due. They were just contemplating splitting up and trying to hitch, when an old army lorry loaded with bales of straw drew near. The driver applied his brakes and finally ground to a halt several yards down the road. It turned out to be one of the farmers from the night before. "Ah can give yis a lift as far as Hexham", called down their saviour, his weathered face beaming down from the cab.

"Yi's wha great last night, ah wish ah had brought wor lass."

Praise indeed thought Terry, slinging his rucksack on to the top of the bales and clambering up after it. "Thanks mate, you're a gentleman."

As soon as the last person's feet left the ground the lorry lurched into motion and they scrambled into position on the top of the tightly packed bales, finding handholds on the securing ropes.

"Well, lads" asked Terry, "di yi think you would go squatting again?"

Johnny, the only one to have somehow kept himself clean, spoke up first. "Very interesting" he said dryly, "ah would say it's very much a summer time occupation"

"It certainly opened up my eyes" enthused Pricey, contemplating his dirty hands, broken finger nails, and now well-weathered wind-cheater."Ahl be back, every chance ah get."

"Just try and stop me", agreed Eric, "this is just the beginning, there's gonna be some great times!"

Terry smiled contentedly, he couldn't wait to hear Eric's version of events recounted in Simpsons that night, he was sure it would be a lot better than reality.

The Kansas City Seven

They would have loved to go squatting every weekend but with the advent of the Downbeat, things were happening in the city. The club's main night was Saturday, the early evening session usually featuring a trad band and finishing at ten thirty, then the place reopened at midnight for an all night session. This was the main attraction for the crowd, no-one wanted to go to bed on a Saturday night. The all night session featured modern jazz usually performed by the M.C.5 featuring leader Mike Carr on organ and his brother Ian on trumpet with Gary Cox on tenor, John O'Carrol, bass, and drummer Ronnie Stephenson. This group were superb musicians, attracting fans from all over the North East, including the majority of other players.

One such fan was young musical phenomenon Jeff Hedley, at seventeen already something of a virtuoso on tenor sax. Jeff, tall and gangly and wearing horn-rimmed specs did not look like a typical jazzman. His favourite tenor player was Lester (Pres) Young and he had somehow acquired a narrow brimmed hat like Pres's which he wore at all times. This, along with a long tweed overcoat made him stand out from the other modern jazz fans with their button down collars and white short Macs. Jeff was a civil servant, and Pricey already knew him, so it wasn't long before he was part of the crowd, impressing everyone with his knowledge of music. Three other musicians who became regular visitors to the all night

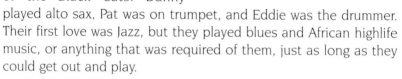

Jeff Hedley at the New Orleans Club

sessions were Danny Okpoti, Pat Odoi, and Eddie Adjei. These were three black guys, originally from Ghana, who were playing bread and butter music around the working men's clubs under the name of the Black Cats. Danny played alto sax, Pat was on trumpet, and Eddie was the drummer. Their first love was Jazz, but they played blues and African highlife music, or anything that was required of them, just as long as they could get out and play.

One night Eric and Danny struck up a conversation about music, and Danny was later to confide that he had never met a white guy who knew so much about blues. Thus far in his life Danny's experience with white people had been negative to say the least, but this was about to change.

Although a great many musical ideas were exchanged, and everyone loved The M.C.5., it has to be admitted that the main attraction of The Downbeat was the fact that you could drink into the small hours, and the presence of a great many attractive young ladies who liked to stay up very, very, late. The whole crowd loved to dance and there was no shortage of partners. Johnny and Terry in particular were always on the lookout for good partners and although dancing was their main preoccupation who knew where it would lead? Their taste in woman was very similar: they were both attracted by beautiful women with slight imperfections, such as slightly bowed legs, or the suggestion of a cast in the eye.

One night their attention was attracted by the superb style of two girls dancing together. The smallest of the two wore a dirndl skirt which spun out parallel with her waist as she danced, exposing perfect, slightly bowed legs. Johnny and Terry split them up immediately, Johnny succeeding in capturing the prize. After the dance was over and they returned to their table, Johnny put the icing on the cake. "You'll never believe it but she's got a cast in her eye as well!"

The poor girl was overwhelmed by the attention she received that night, so much so that eventually she refused to dance with either of them. Eric too was attracted towards girls who were out of the ordinary and when he saw a couple of black girls dancing together he and Dave Wilson intervened. Eric's partner was Doreen Caulker. Eric and Doreen were destined to dance together for a very long time.

At about this time Eric had discovered a new hero. A record by Kansas City blues shouter Joe Turner had been issued in Britain. The LP called "Boss Of The Blues", featured piano player Pete Johnson, already well known by the crowd as

105

resident pianist for Chess records. This was big band blues, with a front line made up of Count Basie side men playing heavy riffs behind Turners powerful vocals. Eric was entranced and as the record did the rounds and other people bought it, so were the rest of the crowd.

If Eric wanted to sing in front of a band like that he didn't have far to look for musicians. Sitting round a table at the Downbeat one night were: drummer Johnny Steel, pianist Alan Price, alto sax player Danny Okpoti, tenor man Jeff Hedley, and trumpeter Pat Odoi. If they could find a bass player there would be seven. And so the Kansas City Seven was born, at least in the heads of these young musicians.

The problem now was to find somewhere to practise, and many nights would be spent sitting round pub tables discussing this, and all the other logistics of running a band. Danny and Pat found themselves with a whole crowd of new friends, all of them white, which for the two Ghanaians was something of a new departure. The question of where to practise finally resolved itself when Eric bumped into Blackie and Jimmy now firmly established with The Gamblers, who had been suffering from the same problem until their manager came up with something suitable. The steep slope of Dean Street which runs down from Collingwood Street to the River Tyne is traversed by a railway viaduct, an awe-inspiring example of Victorian architecture. Railway arches are often used to house small businesses and the citizens of Newcastle were not about to waste this space. The Gamblers were renting the second of three storeys, above an engineering works, the top storey being the province of a wrestling gym. This was an ideal spot as no one lived in the vicinity and noise was not a problem. Somehow they had managed to manhandle an old upright piano up the stairs, also several battered easy chairs and a couple of settees. Along one wall was a worktop with a sink and cooker, there was even an old fridge. The two ends of the arch consisted entirely of windows, grubby and cobwebbed, but still affording wonderful views of the city and the river.

Jimmy introduced Eric to his manager Jack, a slim blonde-haired chap with a confident air. At thirty-four years of age he was considered by The Gamblers to be ancient. They were surprised that he still had his own hair and teeth and showed an interest in young skirt. Jack agreed to let them share the use of the practise room for a nominal sum, and after several false starts they eventually got together for a practise. Although they had still not found a bass player they seemed to gel both as friends and musicians. In an incredibly short time the sound of Joe Turner's "Lipstick, Powder and Paint" was ringing out over Dean Street.

Of course these sessions always included a certain amount - or a great deal - of drinking, and Terry offered his services as beer carrier. He was fascinated and amazed to observe this group of disparate characters quickly turning themselves into a band, playing the kind of music he had never heard live before.

Practising was all very well but it wasn't long before someone suggested that this would be a great place for a party, so when Saturday came along, it was almost a forgone conclusion. After several pints in Simpsons in the afternoon, the band, along with Dave and Terry, headed off with crates of beer to set up the place for the evening. As there was bound to be dancing the floor needed to be cleared and some of the debris of former occupants removed. After their labours they sprawled out on the ragged furniture and sampled some of the beer. Eric took a long swallow from a bottle of Amber and studied the froth appreciatively. "Just one thing missing, lads," he said giving a hearty burp, "we need a record player."

"We've got a radiogram at home" said Johnny, "we could borrow that."

"Hey Johnny", chipped in Terry, "it's enormous, how wi gonna get it here?"

By now the drink was taking effect, nothing seemed a problem. Johnny fixed Terry with an imperious stare. "Be positive Molloy, use your initiative, it can be done! We'll bring it on the bus."

So they walked up to Pilgrim street and took the double-decker for Sheriff Hill. Johhny's mother didn't turn a hair when they announced their plan, only insisting that they have something to eat first. "Don't forget," she said as they carried it down from the second floor, "that radiogram belongs to Rediffusion." we only rent it, 2/6d. a week. "

"Aye, well that includes insurance " replied Johnny.

She laughed, "Not for carrying on the platform of a double-decker bus I'll bet, so go canny."

They were soon sailing back across the Tyne bridge, two youths, perched on the platform of the speeding bus, hanging on to the huge radiogram for which the conductor had charged half fare. It must have been a bizarre sight.

Johnny had grabbed a handful of L.P.s, and once the radiogram was installed he placed his latest acquisition on the turntable. It was "Tomorrow Is The Question" by Ornette Coleman and when the track, "Tears Inside" began, he turned up the volume. For once they listened to recorded music played as loud as it should be, and there was no one to tell them to turn it down. During their absence, Eric and Dave had gone off to the Metropole, an underground coffee bar on Blackett Street where the local talent hung out on Saturday afternoons. They'd spread the word, "a party tonight, meet at Simpsons Buffet, tell your (female) friends", and hoped for the best.

It was now almost opening time so they made their way up Grey Street to the Grape Vaults, to meet the rest of the crowd and sample a few glorious halves of Exhibition to start the evening off. By the time they arrived at Simpsons the place was already throbbing with life. The grapevine in Newcastle was as effective as any village, the word had spread among that section of youth who were party-goers, especially, the lads were pleased to note, the females.

Maureen and Eileen came tottering up the stairs on ridiculously high heels, no doubt there would be a few purple-hearts secreted away in the huge white handbags they both carried. Chas Chandler, Chunkie Bourne, and Alan Carr arrived, Alan toting his carrying case full of Chess singles, guaranteeing great music. The Gamblers appeared along with manager Jack and an entourage of fans.

Once everyone was suitably well oiled, Terry organised a kitty of ten shillings a head which he deposited behind the bar with Mary, to be picked up at closing time in the form of crates of Amber and Brown. Half past ten found them careering down Grey Street carrying crates and singing songs, while most of the city's drinkers were heading for the last bus home.

Johnny's radiogram was soon cranking out rhythm and blues at top volume. The followers of The Gamblers being slavish fans of the current charts were bemused by the choice of music. Floating around in the top ten at that time were Cliff Richard, Bobby Darin, Lonnie Donegan, Paul Anka, and Marty Wilde. What assaulted their eardrums at this party was the music of Ray Charles, Joe Turner, Muddy Waters, Chuck Berry, Little Walter, Bo Diddly, Howling Wolf and Lightning Hopkins. Gradually the party began to thin out and Johnny took charge of the record player, selecting music by Miles Davis, Gerry Mulligan, and John Coltrane. Terry settled down with Maureen on one of the old settees, and they fell asleep to the haunting voice of Billy Holiday singing "Willow Weep For Me".

The thunder of an express train crossing the viaduct woke him early. He peered groggily at his watch, half past eight. He closed his eyes again but the desire for coffee was too great. Taking care not to disturb Maureen he made his way to the sink and after removing an accumulation of bottles and glasses, filled the kettle, plugged it in and turned to survey the scene. Every chair and settee was occupied by sleeping forms and one or two had made do with the floor. What this place needs is a few mattresses he mused, and if everybody brought sleeping bags even better. In the next few weeks various mattresses began to appear, transported by The Gamblers manager Jack, who although reputed to be married didn't seem to spend a great deal of time at home.

The viaduct parties became legendary and the more partying went on the less band practice took place but everyone was having too good a time to worry about it. Having this hideaway in the heart of the city took some of the pressure off Dave and Terry and they found they had less visitors to Heaton Grove. But by then their relations with their landlord had become strained, and they felt that he was looking for an excuse to throw them out. One Friday night they'd got back from town late with Eileen and Maureen in tow. The girls were in a silly mood, and giggled their way up the stairs, racing each other for the toilet on the second landing where they proceeded to make more noise. Dave and Terry were in no better state, and when they reached the attic flat, on went the record player at high volume. A spot of dancing seemed in order and the two couples were draped round each other when the door opened and in walked the landlord. For some reason he was carrying a large torch. "Now then, what's going on here?" he shouted, as if it wasn't plain to see.

The beam of the torch had fixed itself on Eileen's generous breasts. "We are danthing", said Eileen " and you can stop shining that light on my tiths."

Terry's heart sank, they'd had it now. He tried to intervene with a few calming words, but was ignored. "That's it", the landlord's voice was becoming more high pitched. "You can all get out, NOW! The lot of you."

"Juth coth you're not getting any thekth," said Eileen, "you're only jealoth."

By now the landlord was almost apoplectic with rage. "Just give us ten minutes mate", intervened Dave," we'll all get out."

"You've got five minutes", came the reply, as he stormed off down the stairs, "five minutes."

The girls erupted into a fit of giggles as the door slammed behind him. "That's fucked it", said Terry, " what do wi do now?"

"Get the sleeping bags out", replied Dave. "Come on girls, there's a nice comfortable park down the road, it's a nice night, a bit of fresh air'll do you good".

So off they trooped, down to the little park near the station where they slept under the stars. A new experience for the girls and one they seemed to enjoy, at least while they were still under the influence of drink.

The next morning Terry woke them in time to catch their train to work and they staggered on board, lipstick smudged and mascara running down their cheeks, Eileen's beehive hairdo all awry. "What a bonny sight" commented Terry.

"Aye" laughed Dave, "they'll never make squatters, just imagine them on the road with tha high heels and handbags".

The pair headed off to Shields Road to eat breakfast in a cafe before going back to face the landlord who gave them a choice. "Unless you can promise me that you'll have no more women back here you'll have to go."

"Then ah reckon we'll have to go" said Terry. "That's right" agreed Dave, "wi didn't leave home to become celibate, we'll just get wha stuff."

So there they were, sitting on the wall on Heaton Grove surrounded by their meagre belongings. "Where do we go from here?" asked Terry.

"Ah think ay'll go home for a bit before me mother rents me room out" replied Dave.

"Well ahv got the key to the viaduct, ah suppose ah could doss down there for a bit till ah find something else."

"Underneath the arches eh?" said Dave. So they set off towards Shields Road for their respective buses, laden down with gear, singing the old song "Underneath The Arches", secure in their youthful optimism, sure that everything would be alright and of course it was.

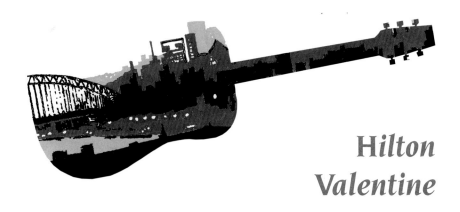

Hilton Valentine

Terry moved into the practice room under the viaduct without any qualms. Living there appealed to his sense of adventure giving him a greater measure of freedom and an acceptable degree of romantic squalor. Maureen and Eileen were less enamoured with his new abode, complaining bitterly at having to negotiate the rickety stairs in their high heels and generally tutting at the dust and dirt.

In the early days of their relationship the girls seemed happy to provide the two boys with sex and purple hearts in equal measure, but as time went by it became apparent that they wanted something more in the way of commitment. Maureen's parents were due to be away from home for a weekend so the two boys were invited to stay. So it was with some misgivings that Dave and Terry found themselves on the train for the coast one Friday night, heading for Whitley Bay.

"At least wha not ganna meet tha parents" said Dave, thrusting his hands deep in the pockets of his combat jacket and staring disconsolately out of the window.

"Aye, yi can stuff that," Terry agreed, "ahm too young ti settle down, never mind, wi might get some decent food cooked for wi."

"Wi might" nodded Dave, "but that just means getting wha feet further under the table."

They sat together in silence surrendering to the rhythm of the tracks, each lost in his own thoughts.

By the time the train reached its destination they had both cheered up considerably. It was some time since either of them had been to the coast, it was Friday night, the weather was fine and there were lots of pubs in Whitley Bay.

The girls met them off the train and they were led away from the sea front along narrow streets until they came to a neat council estate. The pebble-dashed houses were painted white and each had a tiny front garden with privet hedges of startling uniformity. Maureen led the way to number 37, Cullercoats Crescent and glancing round nervously produced a large key and let them in as quietly as possible. As it was still broad daylight, their stealth would hardly conceal them from any nosy neighbours. Terry had already noticed a few twitching curtains, but made no comment. Maureen led the way into the front room which smelled of damp and furniture polish in equal proportions. The room was furnished with a large sideboard, a china cabinet, a radiogram and a dining suite all in dark veneered wood polished until it shone.

The boys had been in homes like this before and knew that this furniture museum would only be used on very special occasions, so they suggested sitting in the kitchen. With some relief, Maureen agreed and the girls soon had the chip pan on and sausages in the frying pan. After a huge meal of sausages, chips, eggs and beans, accompanied by white bread and cups of tea, the boys lounged in front of the coal fire while Maureen and Eileen went off to the bathroom to freshen up.

Dave loosened his belt and groaned "Ahll never get any beer down is after that lot", he complained.

"Aye, it wasn't exactly cordon blue or warrever yi call it", agreed Terry "but ah enjoyed it". Ah wonder what thive got planned for tonight?"

"Thiv got something up tha sleeves", replied Dave, "ahll bet tha planning it right now while thi put on another coat of makeup and polish tha white stilettos."

"Well, am not going to The Spanish City, that's for certain, ah'v grown out of funfairs."

At this point Eileen made her entrance, filling the room with the smell of cheap scent. "Yi needn't worry", she snapped, we're taking you to thee a band, you're not the only wonth who know muthithans."

The band in question turned out to be an outfit called The Wildcats. The venue, The Crescent Club, Cullercoats, C.I.U. Affiliated. Both Dave and Terry hated working men's clubs with their endless bingo, officious committee men and cretinous concert chairmen, but neither of them protested. At least the beer would be cheap.

After the usual hassle of being signed in as non-members and depositing sixpence in the box, the girls led the way to the lounge. The place looked as if it had been recently decorated by someone with shares in Formica. There was plastic laminate on every surface including the walls. Despite this, it still exuded the odour of stale beer, cigarettes, piss and disinfectant, redolent of all clubs. There was already a fair sprinkling of young people in the room, all smartly dressed. Most of the boys wore Italian style suits, shirts with button down collars and slim ties. They turned to stare at the boys, Dave in his combat jacket, Terry in his lumber jacket, both wearing jeans and cowboy boots.

Choosing a table near the door, they sat the girls down and headed for the bar. Taking a good swig of his first pint, Dave looked around him. "Well it looks as if wha popular with the locals."

"Aye" agreed Terry " wi better keep wha eyes open, one thing about working mens clubs there's always plenty of committee men about."

By the time they got back to their table they found the girls had been joined by a blonde youth with a pleasant boyish face who looked vaguely familiar to Terry. Sartorially he did not fit in with his compatriots - he was wearing a rather greasy boiler suit. Eileen introduced him. "Thith is Hilton Valentine, he's the lead guitarist with The Wildcats". "Pleased to meet you", said Dave. "Is this the latest thing in band uniforms?"

Hilton grinned. "Nah, ahve just finished work man, doing a spot of overtime. Ah just wanted to ask Eileen about something."

"Aye, have yi got any purple hearts?" laughed Maureen.

Eileen opened up her voluminous handbag and produced the goods. Hilton indulged in a few more words of small talk, then disappeared back stage. Terry suddenly remembered the band from Dougie's wedding. "Is that his real name?" asked Terry, "or just a stage name?"

"No, it's his real name," she replied, "yiv got Ron Mckenzie on drums Harry Dixon on bass, two vocalists, John Frier and Keith Shields, plus Tappy Wright on rhythm guitar."

"You seem to know a lot about them" remarked Dave.

"That's 'cos she's been out with most of them" smirked Maureen.

Deciding that he did not wish to know what "been out "was a euphemism for, Dave did not pursue this line of questioning.

Before too long the concert chairman was on his feet, going through an excruciatingly boring list of announcements before finally introducing the band. Looking resplendent in fawn mohair suits and winkle picker shoes, they launched into "Blue Suede Shoes" with well-rehearsed precision, then hardly pausing for applause, straight into "Good Golly Miss Molly". The boys were very impressed, especially with Hilton's guitar playing as he ripped out solos with apparent ease.

The girls sipped their gin and oranges grinning smugly, basking in the reflected glory. One more drink and they were all on the dance floor, where they stayed until the band completed their first twenty minute spot. That's what they hated about these clubs, "the turn" did three twenty minute spots interspersed by bingo.

"Ah reckon even if Elvis came and played the place for nowt, he'd have ti fit in between the bingo", complained Terry.

"Aye, they'd stop Frank Sinatra in the middle of his set if the pie and peas arrived. Never mind, the beer's like nectar let's have some more."

They stood at the bar drinking and being shushed by the locals while the girls handled three bingo cards each.

The band's second set kept up the same frenetic pace. Cliff Richards' "Move It" was followed by Eddie Chochran's "Twenty Flight Rock". The dance floor was too packed for comfort so they sat back and enjoyed the music. When the interval arrived, so did the pie and peas, so bingo did not recommence immediately, giving everyone a chance to chat.

Hilton rejoined them at their table along with Tappy Wright. Terry and Dave plied them with questions about the band and discovered that they were playing seven nights a week, also Saturday and Sunday lunchtimes. "Aye, and he works overtime on Sunday" laughed Tappy, "so he's got to crawl past the office on he's hands and knees to get out and play the gig."

"Christ, no wonder you need purple hearts", said Dave, "Yi deserve a medal for that kind of dedication".

As the two musicians stood up to leave, Tappy leaned forward in a confidential manner. "By the way, lads, see that crowd of nutters sat at the table nearest the stage? Tha planning to give you two a right kicking so ahd leave before the end if ah was you."

Confronted with this charming piece of information, they took appropriate action. The band was into its second number when they slid off into the night, feeling glad to have had the foresight to choose a table near the door.

Not feeling inclined to hang around at the bus stop they set off to walk to Whitley Bay, breaking their journey at a roadside pub just in time for a last pint. Once in the resort itself the noise, lights and crowds of the Spanish City drew them in. Soon they were on the waltzer, on the ghost train, eating candyfloss, shooting in the arcades and enjoying all the amusements that they had recently affected to despise.

What better way to end the evening than to walk home eating fish and chips, the beef dripping congealing on one's fingers with the chill of the night air. On arrival at Maureen's house, they tiptoed up the path making loud shushing noises and giggling while she struggled with the huge key. This time they walked straight into the front room and lounged on the three-piece suite still wearing their coats while Maureen turned on the Magicoal electric fire.

Music was the next priority; Dave opened up the front of the big old radiogram that housed the records. The singles were all British, Adam Faith, Cliff Richard, Billy Fury et al. "Ahm not listening to that shite" muttered Dave and began leafing through the LPs finally encountering Frank Sinatra's "Songs For Swinging Lovers". "Let's have Frank, he cried, "at least he can fuckin' sing".

Terry, joining in the spirit of drunken boorishness demanded drink, as if he had not already had enough. Maureen opened up the sideboard and inspected the contents. There was whisky, rum, sherry, port wine, egg flip and various other exotic drinks bought especially for Christmas and never drunk. Terry and Dave settled for whisky, while the girls chose egg flip, a cheap version of Advocaat.

Music can change the mood and Frank Sinatra was singing romantic ballads. The boys cuddled up to the girls and drank the whisky, which tasted wonderfully smooth to their jaded palates. Nature took its course and Dave soon sloped off to bed with Eileen, leaving Terry and Maureen dancing together. "We can sleep in me mum and dad's bed" she whispered, "you go upstairs while ah tidy up."

It was only as he lurched his way upstairs that he realised how drunk he was. The red-eyed white-faced creature staring back at him from the bathroom mirror went in and out of focus. He cleaned his teeth with grim determination in a vain attempt to act normally, but to no avail. His stomach heaved, saliva filled his mouth and he turned to the toilet, just in time. On his knees in front of the bowl, he tasted the soured whisky, as it came back up along with the rest of the contents of his stomach. Resting his forehead on the cool porcelain, he could have stayed there forever, but realising that Maureen would soon be up, he flushed the toilet and went back to his teeth cleaning. Terry entered the master bedroom feeling only marginally better. The room was decorated in what was at that time termed contemporary fashion, i.e. pastel shades of emulsion paint, in this case pink and white. A white laminated dressing table blocked the window, on it lay a vanity set - hand mirror, brush and comb in white and gold - that showed no sign of ever having been used. To complete the illusion of modernity, the bed had a white padded headboard and sported a candlewick bedspread. Slinging his clothes on the floor he crawled into the lumpy bed and closed his eyes, only to open them again as his feelings of nausea increased. He found that the only way to keep the room stationary was to prop himself up against the headboard and stare at a print featuring several kittens adorning the chimney breast. Maureen entered the room looking cool and fresh and for the first time in his life, he saw her without the usual liberal application of panstick, lipstick and mascara.

She wore a pair of Winceyette pyjamas that must have dated from her school days, the fit being so tight that her small breasts strained at the buttons. She looked about fourteen years old and it occurred to Terry for the first time, that she was probably not yet seventeen. He moaned softly and slid further down into the bed. As she switched off the light and clambered in beside him, he felt cold clammy beads of sweat standing out on his forehead. She made to reach out for him but he took her hands in his and addressed her in what he thought was a clear and profound manner, but was in fact a drunken slur.

"Maureen, why don't you stop all this? Why don't you stop taking purple hearts and staying out all night, worrying yah parents? Ahm no good for yi, find yourself a decent bloke and settle down, you're a nice girl."

With that he surrendered into a deep black hole of dreamless sleep and was soon snoring gently. The next morning he woke with the dawn and lay listening to the seagulls squawking on the roof until the desire for coffee and food drove him out of bed and into his clothes. He looked down at Maureen; the buttons on her pyjamas had finally given way, exposing one firm, pink, breast. He paused for a moment as a spasm of desire surged through him, then tucking the blankets up to her chin, he kissed her gently and left the room.

Downstairs he poked the kitchen fire back into life, made tea and toast and sat in front of the flickering flames feeling the life ebbing back into his body, but did not linger for long. He soon had his lumber jacket on and was heading for the back door when he hesitated and made his way to the front room. Opening the sideboard he rummaged among the bottles of port and sherry, located a miniature bottle of brandy, slipped it into his pocket and left by the back door. As the door slammed behind him he knew that something had ended that had never really begun.

Turning up his collar and buttoning up his coat against the sea air, he headed for the station. Leaving the little housing estate behind and taking a route that took in the sea front, he strode along the near empty streets, the seagulls swooping and calling overhead.

Outside the station stood a vendor's barrow selling newspapers. He selected "The Sketch" a paper with a left wing bias, but he did not choose it for its politics. On the back page was a strip cartoon called Peanuts by Schultz and, on the inside, a whole page of cartoons including BC, a surreal strip featuring the hilarious adventures of a group of cavemen.

The Newcastle train was drawn up at the platform and was due to leave in ten minutes. Feeling the need for some sugar in his system, he searched his pockets for a sixpenny piece. Inserting it into the red, cast iron, dispenser bolted to the wall, he pulled out a drawer at the bottom and was rewarded with a bar of Nestlés chocolate. Climbing aboard the train, he walked along the corridor until he found an empty compartment. Sliding the door open he stepped inside and pulled down the blind - a sure deterrent against company.

By the time he had made himself comfortable the train was on the move and was soon clear of the station, allowing the morning sun to filter through the dirty windows, providing some welcome warmth. Unwrapping his chocolate bar he took a bite, followed by a sip of the filched brandy. The train was now racing through the countryside and as the spirit coursed through his veins and the chocolate restored his blood sugar level he began to feel decidedly more human.

Keeping the rest of the brandy for later, he turned his attention to his newspaper, but soon slipped into reverie. He thought about "The Wildcats" and what a professional outfit they were, why did they have to slog it out around the pubs and clubs when far inferior bands made the big time? The reason, he decided, was they were singing songs already made famous by other people. If they could only write their own material, they would have a much greater chance of success, but what band ever did that?

Pondering on the events of last night, he hoped that Dave would forgive him for fleeing the coop, but he gave little thought as to how Maureen might feel. Such is the heartlessness of youth. Sipping at his brandy, the warmth of the compartment made him drowsy and he drifted off to sleep safe in the knowledge that the train terminated at Newcastle Central Station, leaving him with only a ten minute walk to his new home, beneath the very same railway line.

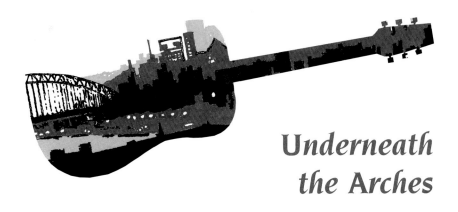

Underneath
the Arches

The idea of living in such an unusual spot appealed to Terry's sense of adventure and somehow the sound of the trains rumbling overhead made him feel secure. Although the Great North Road still ran through the city the traffic was confined to Pilgrim Street and Northumberland Street, so that he could walk to work at seven in the morning, his way only impeded by the occasional delivery van or electric trolley bus swishing its way through the streets driven by overhead cables.

With time on his hands he decided to clean the premises up. The administration of a large tin of white emulsion paint soon brightened up the old yellow distempered walls and once the windows were cleaned and the floor scrubbed it began to have some potential as a home. Or perhaps a place where a band wouldn't mind doing a bit of practising? Anxious for some company he chivvied the band along and they did begin to turn up at reasonably regular intervals.

Pricey was probably the most dedicated and one night during a rather prolonged beer break he made a suggestion. "Look, the only reason wha all hear tonight is because of Terry, why don't whi make him our manager? The Gamblers have got a manager, why can't we have one?"

"That's right" agreed Eric, "what do yi reckon Terry, that's if everybody else agrees."

The rest of the band chorused approval. "What do ah know about managing a band?" protested Terry

"About as much as any of us" said Johnny. "Give it a go."

"All right then, ahll try" agreed Terry, nervously swigging his drink, "ahll give it a go!"

"The first thing you need is a bass player."

For the next week or so Terry made little attempt to manage the band apart from encouraging them to practise. In the line of duty he and Johnny toured round a few likely pubs which featured live music but they were not surprised to find that there was no demand for rhythm and blues, although they did sample a few different beers. They were still regular patrons at the New Orleans Club and were friendly with the owner, a gentleman of Polish extraction named Urick. It occurred to Terry that the club was only used at the weekends, so he approached Urick with a deal. If they could generate enough custom for him to make money on the bar, would he let them have free use of the

Rythmn & Blues

AT

The New Orleans Club

Melbourne Street
(Near The Tanners Arms)

Featuring

The Kansas City Seven

Every Wednesday Night at 7.30

Admission 1/6d

Late Bar

club on a Wednesday night? He agreed on a trial basis, so it was up to them to get as many people there as possible.

Terry knew that art student Stan Atkinson had studied silk screen printing so he persuaded Stan to produce a run of posters advertising the gig. Rhythm and Blues, every Wednesday night, at The New Orleans Club Melbourne Street. Featuring, The Kansas City Seven. Commencing, 7.30. First night Sept. 5th. Admission 1/6d. It was time to do some fly posting. Terry mixed up a bucket full of wallpaper paste and spent his evenings making forays out from the viaduct plastering Newcastle with posters. This clandestine activity appealed to everyone so he had no shortage of helpers and they quickly ran out of posters and places to stick them.

Eric, Danny & Jeff at the New Orleans

Pat plays a solo

They spread the word among their friends, Eric, Johnny and Terry making a special trip to the Old George to persuade The Squatters to attend. The first night was a great success. Terry was on the door raking in the one and sixes, feeling like a real entrepreneur, although he couldn't help noticing when he went upstairs to the club that he knew almost everyone in there. The Squatters enjoyed the music, even Noddy and Spud behaved themselves and Urick could not complain about the bar takings. At interval time Terry sat with Danny and Pat to get their opinion of the evening. The two of them were wreathed in smiles. "I have to tell you Terry", chuckled Danny, "I did not expect such an audience and they were so quiet and well behaved, not like the working mens clubs. This has been a revelation for me"

"Me too" agreed Pat, "Yes, definitely a great success."

It occurred to Terry that, apart from the crew of the Bermuda Star who docked at Newcastle once a year and visited The Newcastle Jazz Club, he had not met any black people. Due to their love of black American music the whole crowd already had a high regard for blacks (the polite term at the time was coloured people), in general, but in the subsequent weeks Danny was to teach them that this in itself was a patronising attitude. "Black people are just people", he would say, "some good some bad" and then with a laugh, "and they don't all have rhythm."

Wednesday night became a regular gig. Johnny's friend Roger Noble joined the band on double bass and other musicians would drop in for

The New Orleans Jazz Club

a blow. Terry had no success in finding them anywhere else to play so he concentrated on persuading them to rehearse and hoped that the word would get round about this great band. This left the weekends free for those who felt the urge to go away with The Squatters again before the winter set in. Not that Alex, Animal and the rest ever let the weather interfere with their plans.

Living at such a pace was a costly business, but luckily for Terry these were affluent times. The post war austerity had given way to an industrial boom and most firms had full order books necessitating the working of a great deal of overtime and he was doing his share. After working a Saturday morning, he was emerging from Bowyers pork shop clutching a couple of pease pudding and saveloy sandwiches, when he observed a familiar figure heading off down Percy Street. A slim girl with short red hair wearing a grey costume - now better known as a suit - with short jacket and tight skirt that showed off her wonderful, undulating little bottom.

It was Hazel. He quickened his pace, speeding up his already fast beating heart. Falling into step beside her, he asked, "Do you have the time please?" She turned towards him and a slight flicker of annoyance in her eyes turned to an expression of joy. "Terry!" she cried, reaching out and falling into his arms.

They kissed unselfconsciously and clung together, then Hazel drew away. "I shouldn't be doing this" she said, glancing round, "I'm a married woman".

"Married! Well, ah suppose ah shouldn't be suprised, you were engaged the last time we met".

They turned down Blacket Street past the Eldon Square, Hazel plying him with information about the wedding, the house in Gosforth, the car and her husband's good job. She was on her way to Fenwicks to do some shopping, Terry was heading for the viaduct to do some eating.

When he told her of his temporary lodgings, she immediately expressed a desire to see the place, so they went off down Grey

Street together, although not physically holding hands, spiritually entwined. They reached the railway arches and ignoring the stares of the car mechanics on the first floor he ushered her upstairs and began making coffee while she inspected the place. A huge old settee was facing the window which gave a view of the city, so there they sat, warmed by the afternoon sun, drinking coffee, Terry having politely put his sandwiches to one side.

Hazel stood up to get a better view and removed her jacket, hanging it neatly on a mike stand. She was wearing a red short-sleeved lambswool sweater. Silhouetted against the window, he thought her breasts looked fuller. He stood up beside her and put his arm around her shoulders. Without hesitating she kissed him tenderly and they clung together breathing in the warmth of each other's bodies. Slowly they sank to the settee then kissed again, this time with urgent passion. Terry broke away for a moment, "Hazel, I'm sorry I havn't got." He hesitated.

"Don't worry", she murmured, "you can't do any harm, I'm already pregnant, why do you think I got married?"

Before he could digest this piece of information she kissed him again and whatever glimmer of conscience he may have possessed quickly dissolved. They made love with reckless abandon, safe in the knowledge that no one could hear or see them except the old city itself. A mote-filled shaft of sunlight shone down on Hazel's crumpled grey skirt and red sweater abandoned on the dusty floor, and her black silk panties had somehow contrived to land on the mike stand. This being the days before the invention of tights she was still wearing her suspender belt and stockings, but nothing else.

Terry pulled the coloured blanket from the back of the settee to cover their nakedness and they lay together basking in the blissful sanity that follows love making. He slowly became aware that she was sobbing quietly, her head buried against his chest. "What's the matter pet, what's wrong?"

"You're so free", she said, "and now I'm trapped. What have I done?"

His mind raced for an answer. "You don't want this kind of life if you're really honest, yi need security, status, money, you're going to have a baby, you'll be happy."

She lay beside him for a while and then brushing her tears away gathered up her clothes.

"Do you have a toilet?" While she was gone he got himself dressed, put on the kettle and absent mindedly tidied up the place. He didn't have long to wait, Hazel soon reappeared. Her tears were gone, new makeup had been applied and she looked as immaculate as ever. "Well, I'm off to Fenwicks to spend some of his money. I'll see you soon, Terry".

She kissed him gently on the cheek, her hand brushed through his hair, then she headed for the stairs. "If you ever need me", he called after her, "you can ring me at work, Andrew Reids."

He heard her reply "Okay", but she was already down the first flight of stairs, leaving him to his coffee and two very cold and soggy pease pudding sandwiches. These he cast aside, then, laying on the settee, he pondered on the ways of woman until the steady beat of the trains overhead lulled him to sleep.

Danny and Pat were by now totally assimilated into the crowd and as older people - in their late twenties - they tended to take an almost paternal interest in the doings of this bunch of kids. During the week money was tight and pubs were expensive so Danny issued an invitation to all and sundry to visit him and Pat at their home in the west end of Newcastle.

There were three notorious streets in that part of town: Rye Hill, East Parade and West Parade. In Victorian times these huge terraced houses accommodated the wealthy members of Newcastle society, now it housed what polite society called the dross. Danny and Pat had no choice but to live there, as racism was so ingrained that they would not have been welcome in many other parts of town. Although there were only a small number of blacks and Asians in Newcastle at that time, ghettoisation had already begun.

As they walked down East Parade, it seemed to the romantic minds of the boys that these houses were similar to the brown stone tenements of New York that they had seen in so many films, with the same type of steps leading up to the front door, suitable for sitting out on during long summer evenings. Indeed, there were a couple of people sitting on the steps of number eight drinking brown ale and looking suitably unconventional. A man wearing a large black hat and sporting a neckerchief and a woman dressed in gypsy attire. They watched with interest as the boys walked past. Number nine East Parade had once been the residence of the lord mayor of Newcastle, now it was home to a very disparate group of people.

Every city has at least one infamous family living on the edge of society who have become a law unto themselves. In Newcastle it was the Doyles. This notorious clan made a living as unlicensed barrow boys, scrap collectors, and various other illegal or downright criminal activities. They were best known for their propensity for casual violence and total disrespect for the law. The basement of number nine housed one strand of this family and the matriarch and patriarch of the whole brood were lolling on the steps next door.

Danny and Pat took up the front room, on the ground floor, looking out over what had once been the gardens of these stately houses, now a wasteland of brambles and broken fences. In the back room lived Eddie, a venerable old black man, still spry at eighty plus, who seemed to live on a diet of fish and chips washed down with brown ale and was always ready to tell the tale of his colourful past in the merchant navy.

Upstairs lived the Ridley family renamed by Terry as the Rickets family. Mrs Rickets was a tall grey-haired woman of indeterminate age, hair permanently in curlers, cigarette clamped in her mouth.

Years of sitting in front of the fire had given her stockingless legs the mottled appearance known as corned beef legs and she wore a seemingly permanent uniform of wrap-around pinny and slippers. Her life was devoted to the welfare of her three sons, two hulking blonde-haired brutes in their late twenties and one snivelling wretched child of about ten years old. There was no sign of a Mr Rickets. Finally, in the attic lived a tiny old man who only put on an appearance on pension days.

Jeff Hedley, Johnny, Eric and Terry became regular visitors, taking delight in the fact that they were in a part of town where others would fear to tread. They would sit drinking tea and discussing music, or Danny would play a soulful blues on sax accompanied by Pat's muted trumpet, transporting them all onto another plane of existence. Something that helped this process along was the use of marijuana. The boys had of course read about the drug in "On The Road" and many other books, but so far it was something outside their experience. To Danny and Pat, smoking dope was as natural as drinking tea and they made regular trips to Manchester for their supply. The first time Pat rolled a joint and passed it round they all expected something mind blowing, but they soon learned to relax and enjoy its mellowed-out effects.

One Tuesday night, Eric and Terry were enjoying Danny and Pat's hospitality. Danny was sitting on the broad windowsill looking out onto the street when he spotted something that caused him some concern. "It looks to me as if there is going to be some trouble, the landlord has come for the rent."

They crowded to the window. A battered blue Dormobile was drawn up at the kerb and the driver, a middle-aged Asian gentleman slid open the door and stepped down. At the same time a younger man alighted onto the pavement and looked around him nervously. The driver went to the rear of the van, opened the back doors, and six more Asians of various shapes and sizes disembarked. "It's Mr Singh" said Pat. Those Doyles downstairs haven't paid any rent for over a year, and they're using the doors for firewood. I'd guess he's come to evict them"

"Couldn't he go through the proper channels?" asked Eric.

Pat laughed his characteristic giggle. "There are no proper channels for people round here, the authorities would just ignore you, you have to deal with things for yourself."

By now Mr Singh and his brothers were in the house. Their footsteps could be heard in the hall and clattering down the carpetless stairs to the basement. Terry could almost smell the fear and excitement in the air as they all waited for the next move. Obviously the landlord had long ago given up negotiating with the Doyles: this was outright warfare and he was determined to win.

A great deal of swearing, scuffling and banging ensued, but eventually the two Doyle brothers were out on the street. It took a great deal longer to evict the woman and children. Mr Singh and his brothers were sporting a great many scratches and bites before the place was cleared.

The Doyle brothers were by now next door, rallying the rest of the clan, and they soon emerged from number eight, led by the father who looked distinctly unfriendly and was brandishing an iron bar. The Doyles, no strangers to this type of incident, were kitted out with weapon in the form of pick-axe handles, no doubt hollowed out and filled with lead, suitable for the occasion. They proceeded to break down the door, the patriarch making good use of his iron bar. Suddenly the door opened and two pairs of hands grabbed him. In the ensuing struggle Mr Singh sustained a blow to the head but they managed to drag the old devil inside. Now they had a hostage. Blood pouring from his wound, Mr Singh called through the letter box, "You must desist or it will be the worse for your father. Danny and Pat went out into the hall and came back with an exhausted Mr Singh. They sat him down and staunched the flow of blood with towels. "We are trapped in here" cried out Pat, "I hope someone has called the police, here is a man who badly needs to go to the hospital."

Making sure they could not be seen from the street, Eric and Terry watched the scene outside. The frustrated Doyle family were venting their spleen on Mr Singh's Dormobile, attacking it with iron bars, hatchets, bricks and anything else that came to hand, and some of the other denizens of the street had emerged to join in the fun. It wasn't long before someone thought of dropping a match into the petrol tank and the resulting explosion lit up the whole area.

Two Black Marias came clanging down the street, followed by two squad cars, an ambulance following close behind. The police were obviously taking no chances with a disturbance on East Parade. The vehicles disgorged their contents of uniformed men who began to indiscriminately throw anyone they could lay their hands on into the back of the paddy wagons. Eventually a sergeant accompanied by several constables came up the steps of number nine. He hammered on the door with his truncheon. "I believe you have a Mr Doyle in there with you. Could you hand him over please?"

The door was opened by one of the young Asians and they were promptly arrested and thrown into the Black Marias with their former adversaries. Judging the time to be right, Danny went out and informed the sergeant of Mr Singh's plight and he summoned up the ambulance men who quickly stretchered him out. The sergeant's gaze fell on Eric and Terry. "Well, ah don't know what the hell you two lads are doing here and ah don't want to know, yis better get yourselves off home, you don't belong around here."

Thankfully they fled and headed down Elswick Road for the city at a very brisk pace, only slowing down when they reached the Black Bull. They were soon inside, downing pints like miners after a hard shift. "If that's Tuesday night" said Eric, "ah wonder what it's like at the weekend."

"Ah don't know", replied Terry, "probably human sacrifice and cannibalism, one thing's certain, ah don't intend to find out."

Although he did not realise it at the time, Terry was soon to know East Parade very well indeed.

9 East Parade

Eric, never very keen on going home, spent the night at the viaduct with Terry and the pair of them planned a party for Friday night. With only three days to put the word out, it was remarkably well attended, perhaps a little too well for Terry's taste, he wondered how long it would be before there was trouble, or the police put on an appearance. The next day, his forebodings proved to be justified. While he and a few of the others were tidying up, they suddenly became aware of a presence. Two very large men, whom he recognised as wrestlers from the gym upstairs, were in their midst. With the quiet confidence of the self possessed, one of them spoke. "Ah want yis all out of here for good by this afternoon, or yi'll be gettin' carried out"

"But why?" asked Terry. "Somebody's been shaggin' in wha wrestling ring" said the other one. "But how do you know", asked Pricey. "Cos it's covered in spunk stains" said the first, anger now creeping into his tone.

Everyone wanted to laugh but no-one did. "Is that your final word?" asked Eric, but the pair marched out without another word or a backward glance.

Everyone knew that this was the end. They had to act fast. Luckily a couple of The Gamblers were present, so Jimmy Crawford rang their manager to bring the van round to remove the piano and any other essential gear. Even the persuasive Jack realised there was no point in arguing, the die was cast. It was not until they were all sitting round a table in Simpsons that it occurred to Terry that he was homeless again.

Everyone offered him a few nights bed and board while he looked around but Danny came up with something more concrete. "Why not come and live at East Parade? Now that the Doyles have been removed Mr Singh will be looking for new tenants to occupy the basement. I'm sure a nice white boy who has a regular job will suit him fine."

For some perverse reason the idea of living in such an unsavoury neighbourhood appealed to Terry and the rest of the crowd were equally enthusiastic. So, a few pints later he set off with Danny and Pat to view the premises and meet his prospective landlord.

As he walked down East Parade, Terry was amazed at the diversity of the street. Some of the houses were tidy and neat with their metal railings still intact, others were filthy and run down with front gardens strewn with debris. One immaculate house had been converted into a convent and the bizarre sight of a huge crucifix dominating the front garden appealed to Terry's sense of the absurd. "Who needs to travel to foreign climes?, thought Terry, "plenty of missionary work round here."

When they came to number eight, Mrs Doyle was sitting on the step. No other Doyles were in sight - Terry surmised that most of the men would be in jail. In front of number nine, the blackened tarmac bore testimony to the recent blaze and distorted tyres decorated the tiny garden. No doubt any metal parts had been converted into bottles of brown, one of which was clutched in Mrs Doyles' ringed hands at that very moment. There was very little left of ten East Parade. The house, having been abandoned at some time, was now in the process of being dismantled by the local urchins and would soon be a gap in the rotting teeth of the street. Dropping off Terry's gear in Danny and Pat's room, they descended to the basement on what was left of the stairs. "They burnt them", commented Pat, noting Terry's wondering expression, "along with the doors."

Indeed, the door of the front room was gone along with all the cupboard doors, even the skirting boards had been removed, yet standing there among the debris was a piano in decent condition. Terry stared at it in amazement, "how come they didn't burn this?" Danny ran his fingers over the keys. "It was here when they came. Their little girl Trixie, she could play it".

Terry was nonplussed, pianos and little girls named Trixie did not fit in with drunkenness, violence and burnt skirting boards. He was entering a strange world. The back room was in a slightly better condition, at least the door was still intact, as were the wooden shutters on the windows. There was a sink and gas cooker, both in filthy condition but fully operational. He decided he could make something of this place.

The next step was to approach the landlord, so off they went up Elswick Road to where Mr Singh ran a butcher's shop and general store. He had been in need of over thirty stitches in his recent encounter with the Doyles and still looked the worse for wear, but was remarkably cheerful for all that. He would rent the room for twenty-five shillings a week and required no money in advance. If Terry would visit the local second-hand shop and buy suitable furniture he would pay the bill. Terry promised to decorate the place and began clean-up operations that very afternoon. Johnny had taken a job in the decorating department of Bainbridges while looking for something in his own trade of technical illustrating so was able to provide materials at a discount as well as advising on the decor.

Together they worked on the room and within a week they had achieved a startling transformation using the latest pastel shades of emulsion paint and a very expensive wallpaper. The shabby settee was covered with a colourful blanket, bright prints adorned the walls, and they even purchased a couple of potted plants to complete the picture. The furniture that Terry had chosen needed some attention but it was sturdy old stuff of the kind most people were throwing out in favour of shoddy modern rubbish that would fall to pieces as quickly as it went out of fashion. With a view to a possible sex life he purchased an old brass double bed with a decent mattress for a give-away price, with a patchwork quilt thrown in for good measure.

On the evening that the room was complete, he and Johnny went round to notorious Dodds Arms on West Parade for a celebratory drink. A glance round at the clientele convinced them not to stay long, so they bought half a dozen bottles of brown and headed back. Terry stopped off at the corner shop to buy a paper sack of coal and a bundle of sticks. The nights - as the saying goes - were cutting in and there was a chill in the air. Once back he practised his fire lighting skills, while Johnny attended to the record player. In a short time they were enjoying the warmth of the flames while drinking a toast in brown ale and listening to the magical voice of Billy Holiday singing "I'll Cover The Waterfront".

Life on East Parade took on a steady rhythm. Terry could walk to work and on the way back would stop off at the local corner shop and purchase his food needs for that day, enjoying the process of choosing and preparing for a solitary meal. Mr and Mrs Doyle were often at their post as he walked past, sitting on the steps of number eight with its boarded up windows and empty door frame. The couple seemed to bear him no ill will and would always give him a cheerful wave, usually with a hand clutching a brown ale bottle. On his trips to the off licence he would drop them off the occasional bottle, working on the theory that they would make better friends than enemies.

He was not surprised to find that they had no electricity nor any running water. The latter was evidenced by the fact that the child Trixie made frequent visits to the big Belfast sink on the landing of number nine to fill a huge galvanised bucket with water which only Trixie herself showed any evidence of having used for washing purposes. Terry was fascinated by the self-possessed little girl and although she did not invite conversation they gradually developed some kind of rapport, a tacit accord of mutual respect. Occasionally he would hear her in the basement picking out simple tunes on the piano, causing him to wonder what kind of person she would have been had she been born into a better environment.

The band continued to play the New Orleans club every Wednesday but Terry had no success in finding them any other gigs. The trouble was that the followers of traditional jazz - who tended to be musical bigots - considered the Kansas City Seven's music to be rock and roll and the rock and roll fans looked upon it as jazz. No one thought - least of all the band themselves - that music inspired by the same roots would in the very near future be dominating the music charts and filling the clubs throughout the country.

Their eviction from the viaduct meant they were once more without a rehearsal room and it occurred to Terry that the empty room in the basement would be an ideal spot if they could only sound proof the place. There was a well-established myth in musical circles that egg boxes on the ceiling and walls prevented sound from escaping. As the Steel family owned a shop which sold large quantities of eggs, Johnny and Terry approached Mrs Steel with the request that she save all the large egg boxes in which the eggs were delivered. The kind lady - who already considered them to be insane - concurred and with the lavish application of Evostick they gradually transferred these mundane items to the ceiling of the basement. Alan Price put on an appearance with a tuning fork and spanner, managing to get the piano into some kind of tune, and they were ready for their first rehearsal.

Everyone turned up one Thursday night, and since Danny and Pat lived above and Terry was in the adjoining room, they had no complaints about noise. These sessions took place as often as Terry could persuade the whole band to attend, which was not very often.

One Wednesday night Eric turned up at the New Orleans with Doreen Caulker, the girl he had recently met at The Downbeat. Apparently he had been seeing her ever since but was only now ready for her to meet his friends and of course listen to him sing. Doreen was an instant hit with the whole crowd, girls as well as boys, and it was fairly obvious that the pair were very much in love. Eric was so besotted that it brought out his jealous streak and he would glower from the stage if any of the boys talked to Doreen while he was performing. This of course was a great mistake. They realised there was some sport to be had and took turns chatting her up while Eric fumed.

Doreen Caulker

Christmas 1959 was a couple of weeks away and it was almost the beginning of the new decade that would later become known as the Swinging Sixties. The musical charts of the latter days of the dreary Fifties showed no sign of the musical revolution to come:

1. What Do You Want - *Adam Faith*

2. What Do You Want To Make Those Eyes At Me For - *Emile Ford*

3. Oh Carol - *Neil Sedaka*

4. Travellin' Light - *Cliff Richard*

5.   Seven Little Girls Sitting In The Back Seat - *Avons*

6.   Red River Rock - *Johnnie and the Hurricanes*

7.   Put Your Head On My Shoulder - *Paul Anka*

8.   Snow Coach - *Russ Conway*

9.   Rawhide - *Frankie Laine*

10.   More and More Party Pops - *Russ Conway*

It was the season for parties and Terry had a batch of handbills printed which they scattered around every pub they visited, resulting in the band playing a few extra gigs over the festive season. Danny and Pat played occasionally with a Highlife band at King's College and Johnny was doing the rounds, depping for drummers at working mens clubs and concert parties. Eric would sing with any of the local bands that would have him, notably "The Mighty Joe Young Band" who recorded a private L. P. with Eric featuring on several tracks.

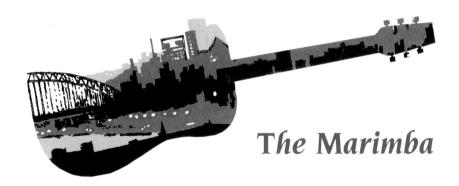

The Marimba

Winter dragged on and by the end of February the whole crowd were feeling in need of a party. Terry suggested the basement of East Parade. He had managed to fit a new door and with the egg boxes on the ceiling it should be fairly sound-proof.

What constituted a good party among this group of hedonists was one that did not run out of beer and had no gate crashers. To this end, Terry made a list of guests and collected ten shillings from each. Girls came free. Danny and Terry bought the beer in the afternoon: they did not consider it a wise move to come rolling down East Parade on a Saturday night carrying crates of beer. It was locked in Danny's cupboard: the party would be after the New Orleans Club.

Terry left the club early to get things ready, i.e. get a fire going in the hearth, transport the beer from its hiding place and plug in the record player. All this could have been done later but he was responsible for the success of the party and just a little nervous. Gradually the party-goers arrived, including Chas Chandler and Alan Carr, the latter carrying his magic box of Chess records. As everyone had already consumed a good deal of drink, things quickly warmed up and before long - to paraphrase Louis Jordon - "The Joint Was Jumping".

Stan Atkinson had brought his camera along and was snapping

away at regular intervals and Eileen was making sure no-one fell asleep by passing out the purple hearts. "What'd I Say" by Ray Charles was receiving its third hearing of the evening when the newly-hung door swung open with a great deal of force and in stepped the Rickets brothers. They were both wearing powder-blue suits and malevolent expressions and showed every sign of being very drunk. The sight of this bunch of scruffy Beatniks in the company of a bevy of gorgeous females - their own attempts at going out on the pull obviously having failed miserably - was like a red rag to a pair of testosterone laden bulls.

They plunged into the thick of the dancers and began dragging people towards the door, shouting "Ger oot if here yi fuckin' noisy bastards" and various other requests for the company to leave the premises. The elder brother took hold of Pat and made to throw him out, but Pat stood his ground. "Take your hands off me man" he ordered, transferring his cigarette to his mouth, leaving his hands free to remove the large paw from his shoulder. The paw refused to be removed and this was where Rickets senior made a grave mistake. Although small in stature Danny and Pat were not the kind of people to allow themselves to be pushed around. They had both been respected amateur boxers back in Ghana, a fact that the two bullies were about to discover. Without wasting any more breath, Pat delivered a short left jab to the stomach of his assailant, followed by a right to the same spot causing him to double up in pain. His cigarette still clamped between his lips, Pat stepped behind the seriously winded yob and effecting an arm lock propelled him out of the room.

Danny dealt with the younger brother, driving him out of the room with a series of light taps designed to subdue rather than damage the youth. The door had not been closed for long when the two brothers returned brandishing wooden spindles smashed from the bannisters. This time they lacked the element of surprise and the whole crowd set about them, driving them back up the stairs, and breaking a few more spindles in process.

An impasse was reached on the first landing with the two brothers holding off all comers on the narrow stairs. The confrontation turned into a slanging match and both sides were becoming bored with the whole business when the familiar sound of the bell on a Black Maria silenced them all. A coterie of burly constables with truncheons at the ready poured in through the open front door, followed by a sergeant whom Terry recognised from the last fracas in East Parade.

Once they realised that this was not a very serious incident they relaxed and put away their weapons. The sergeant soon had the brothers upstairs and the rest of them back down in the basement. "Now then lads, who rang the police?" he asked trying to sound stern.

"It was not us" replied Danny, "We have not got a phone"

"It might of been the young brother upstairs or Mrs Rickets", chipped in Terry, "they've got a phone."

"Anyway", said the sergeant, "We thought it was the Doyles again so tha's two Black Marias and a squad car outside. You'd better tell the rest of the lads to get back to the station, Billy", he said addressing one of the constables.

Then turning to Terry, "Ah see you've got brown ale there, son."

Several bottles of brown later the police left, instructing them to keep the noise down and warning against any future parties. "Imagine what would have happened if the Doyles had gatecrashed", said the sergeant, " it could have got really nasty".

Terry realised that they were right, also that future rehearsals in the basement would probably not be a good idea, so once again the band had nowhere to practise, but then, apart from Wednesday nights, they had nowhere to play so perhaps it did not matter too much.

By this time, the Downbeat had become a well established venue, the all night sessions being particularly popular. It soon became obvious that owner Mike Jeffries had a very relaxed approach to running a night club and people took to bringing sleeping bags and crashing out on the floor in the early hours of the morning, rather than trying to get home on the all night bus which circled the town throughout the wee small hours. Taxis were in short supply and expensive in those austere days, so night owls depended on this nocturnal form of transport which would eventually get you somewhere near home for the set fare of 6d.

Such a success was the Downbeat that Jeffries was branching out into other fields. He was in the process of turning an old shop on Bridge Street into a coffee bar cum bistro with a policy of featuring live music. The place was to be called The Marimba and little Joe Pharoe was recruited to paint the illuminated sign. Joe had no experience in painting signs, nor anywhere to do the work, so he turned to Terry for help.

So it was that one Friday afternoon they purchased a piece of glass five feet long and eighteen inches wide at a glazier's on Elswick Road then carried it gingerly down East Parade. Once in the basement of number nine Joe set about painting his masterpiece and a great deal of time, paint and white spirit was expended without a satisfactory result being achieved. Eventually, Terry suggested a trip to the pub and after several pints they returned with a renewed sense of purpose.

Terry cleaned up the glass and keyed it with a piece of fine sand paper and Joe set to work, this time using a paint designed for touching up car bodywork. The drink must have inspired him for in a comparatively short time the job was complete. This called for a celebration, so more drink was consumed and though it was now approaching midnight it seemed a perfectly rational idea to deliver the sign to the Marimba. Off they went to walk the two miles into town carrying the glass between them in an exaggeratedly careful manner and telling each other to "Go steady" at regular intervals. After a while they became more cavalier and speeded up their pace, narrowly avoiding lamp posts and other pedestrians. The confidence of drunkeness kept them safe and they arrived at Marimba with the sign, and themselves, still intact.

Mike Jeffries settled up with Joe and treated them both to a plate of spaghetti bolognaise and a glass of wine which they considered to be pretty exotic fare. In a city still shruging off the austerity of the post war years, The Marimba itself was considered to be exotic and would prove to be another meeting place for the crowd, plus a source of employment for Alan Price and Johnny Steel.

Joe decided to sleep at East Parade and, as they walked back together in the early hours, the night air was warmer than of late, Spring was on the way and Terry's thoughts turned away from the city and onto the countryside. Time to get back on the road.

Down among the Sand Dunes

The next morning he rose early and after breakfasting with Joe, who had to rush off to some part-time work silk-screening signs for a supermarket, he pulled out his rucksack and began to check his gear.

He aired out his sleeping bag and repaired the torn cover, cleaned up his mess tins and made sure his tiny Primus stove was in working order. Packing the rucksack neatly he included his sheath knife, torch, change of clothes and a small amount of food. Levi jeans had just become available in Britain and Terry had a pair as yet unworn, un-weathered and un-shrunk. These were packed with a view to breaking them in during the course of the weekend. He put on his thick socks and cleaned his hiking boots, pulling them on and turning the white socks over the ankles. Donning his black leather jacket and slipping his wallet into the inside pocket, he was ready for the road.

The sun was warming the front of the building when he stepped out onto the front steps in time to witness a dramatic cameo of life on East Parade. The waste land across the street had once been walled gardens belonging to the residents and in the past had sported huge double cast iron gates. These had long since disappeared but the ten foot tall ornate metal gateposts still remained. The Doyle family were obviously short of money for they were in the process of trying to remove the said gateposts. A stout rope had been attached to the top of one post and the other end fastened to the rear of their scrap collecting lorry. While two of the Doyles excavated the base of the post another revved the lorry in an attempt to topple the rusting pile of cast iron. Terry decided it was going to be a long job and was just about to set off when he spotted another absorbing little scene.

A tiny boy, no more than three years old and wearing nothing but a filthy vest, was occupied in heaving a huge rock onto the low wall that encompassed the abandoned front garden. Terry watched in fascination as he rolled the rock along the wall, his baby teeth gritted with the effort. The intended destination of this potential missile soon became apparent. A toy pedal car was parked against the wall. The owner was probably helping the other little children to dismantle number ten where slates could be heard crashing into the back yard. The infant obviously had a score to settle with the owner of this vehicle, or perhaps he resented the others affluence, at any rate when he'd positioned the rock to his satisfaction he heaved it off the wall and it crushed the bonnet of the tiny car with an impressive crump. He did not hang around to see the reaction to this act of vandalism but made off up the road as fast as his dirty little legs would carry him. "And ah thought the Squatters were hard" reflected Terry, "Ah wonder which prison he'll end up in?"

Swinging his rucksack over one shoulder he set off towards the Haymarket and the Great North Road. He'd heard one of The Squatters mention Alnwick during the week, perhaps that's where they'd be. A couple of good lifts later he alighted in the market square of this pleasant old town in time to find Hank and Alex waiting at the bus stop for Seahouses. Hank had a new companion, a huge wolf-like red-haired dog with a mane like a chow and a large bushy tail.

Without waiting to be asked, Hank launched into the history of the dog whom he had named Willy for no obvious reason. It seemed he had heard the animal howling while making his way home through the back lanes of Gateshead one Saturday afternoon. He traced the sound to a coalhouse in someone's backyard, and on opening the door was attacked by a starving vicious creature showing every sign of having been regularly beaten. Despite any evidence to the contrary, Hank did have a heart and, locking the dog back inside, he headed for the nearest butcher's to buy a bag of lites (cows, entrails). With the aid of the food and a dustbin lid full of water he gradually won the dog over and was soon able to slip a piece of clothesline round its neck and lead it away. "What about the owner?" asked Terry. "Whey, ah knocked on his door and explained that he wasn't fit to own a dog" said Hank. "What did he say to that?" "Not much," came the reply, "its a bit hard to talk when yiv just had a smack in the mouth."

A bus arrived during the telling of this tale and they were soon weaving their way along the country lanes towards Seahouses.

On arrival they stashed their gear in the sandunes near a sign which read: NATIONAL TRUST PROPERTY STRICTLY NO CAMPING and

Alex & Co. in the sand dunes at Seahouses

146

set off for the Bamburgh Castle Hotel where they met up with Animal, Spud, Noddy, Geronimo and a few other lads unknown to Terry. Although Animal and co. were wild they never gave Terry any reason to fear them, but there were some on the periphery of The Squatters that were downright wicked. Most of these seemed small in stature and a great many of them seemed to answer to the name of Frankie. Terry took to referring to them as "the Frankies". One thing was sure, whenever they were around there would always be trouble.

There seemed to be a marked absence of rucksacks this year, rolled up sleeping bags had become de rigueur. Alex explained that Animal had read a book on hoboes, or bindle stiffs, in America who carried a bedroll or bindle, so he had decreed that rucksacks were out, bindles were in. Terry made a mental note to look around for a better sleeping bag.

The Bamburgh Castle Hotel looks out onto the harbour so they bagged the tables by the window and looked out on what was then a busy scene where large quantities of fish - particularly herring - were regularly landed.

It seemed that brown ale alone was not strong enough for the Squatters, so they had taken to making an addition of their own. Alex had procured some pure alcohol from sources unknown and they'd taken to pouring a quantity of this into the bottom of the glass before topping up with beer. Terry decided that whether it looked soft or not he was going to give this one a miss, so he declined the proffered bottle of clear liquid, to the anticipated jeers from the rest. The afternoon took its drunken course and the behaviour became wilder and more raucous until some kind of incident became almost inevitable. For some reason, he did not feel part of the action so he suggested to Geronimo - who having partaken of the pure alcohol was looking distinctly wobbly - that they slip away before closing time.

The rest of the crowd did not see them leave, having decided that swathing themselves in the fishing nets that adorned the walls and wearing lobster pots as hats was a particularly good idea. The two quitters bought fish and chips and headed for their gear stashed on the south beach which, being National Trust land, was usually deserted. The afternoon was unusually hot for the north east coast, ideal weather for breaking in a new pair of jeans, so Terry slipped off the rest of his clothes, struggled into his brand new Levi's and headed for the sea, leaving Geronimo, never one for exposing his flesh to the sun - even though his dark skin would have tanned easily - slumped down in the dunes, cigarette in hand.

He ran in and out of the sea, rolled in the sand to cause maximum abrasion, then ran into the sea again. The crashing waves, hot sun and sheer exuberance of physical exercise had an hypnotic effect and he carried on running up the beach until Geronimo was a black dot in the distance. As he trotted back allowing the sun to dry, and hopefully fade, his jeans he spotted two other figures with his friend.

As he drew nearer, he discerned that these were female forms and very agreeable forms at that. Slowing down his pace so as not to appear too exhausted, he studied the two girls. One was tall and slim with short blonde hair and boyish hips, the other was smaller with a more curvaceous figure and shiny auburn hair down to her waist. They both wore tight black jeans and equally tight sweaters.

As he drew nearer, the smaller of the two turned towards him and laughed. "The creature from twenty thousand leagues beneath the sea, I presume. What do you think you're doing swimming with your clothes on?"

"Maybe you'd like to join me" countered Terry, "ah reckon a good dip in the sea would curb your lip."

"Oh no!" she screamed in mock terror, "I'm heading for the hills."

So saying, she made a run for the sand-dunes with Terry pounding along behind her, appreciating her tight little buttocks as he ran. Finally he brought her to the ground with as close an approximation to a rugby tackle as he could manage. This was achieved at the top of a sand-dune and the momentum caused them to roll down the other side together, giggling as they went.

They landed on a patch of grass - nibbled to almost lawn-like smoothness by the local rabbit population - their arms wrapped around each other, faces inches apart. He looked down into her dark brown eyes smiling back up at him and it seemed natural to kiss her generous mouth. She responded with a passion that caused his already fast-beating heart to pound in his chest. The kiss went on and on, her tongue slipped into his mouth. Without really thinking about it, he slid his hands under her sweater, up her naked back and with unaccustomed ease loosened her bra.

Released from their bondage, her breasts remained firm against his chest. Relinquishing any attempt at subtlety he pushed up her sweater at the front to reveal breasts of such awe inspiring size, beauty and symmetry that he could only stare in breathless wonder. This hiatus gave her time to take charge of the situation . She sat up and pulling down her sweater said "I don't believe wc've been introduced".

Relieved to see an amused twinkle in her eye, he grinned in what he hoped was an appealing fashion. "Sorry, ah just got carried away. Me name's Terry and ah think ahm in love."

"I'll bet" she replied. "Well, I'm Helen, pleased to meet you, now let's see if you're as good at fastening bras as you are at loosening them."

With that, she turned her back and rolled up her sweater proffering the two ends of her sturdy white bra which he fastened slowly, admiring her smooth olive skin and noting the dark mole on her left shoulder blade.

"I suppose you're one of The Squatters" she stated, apparently unconcerned by his tardiness.

"Sort of" came the reply, "more of an apprentice you might say."

"That makes sense," she said, "if you'd been the genuine article I'd have had to beat you off with a stick."

"Well, you've left your mate with one of them" said Terry, "he's not half as polite as me."

"Val can look after herself" replied Helen getting to her feet, "anyway, she knows Geronimo very well indeed."

They set off along the beach together, heading towards Beadnell and away from where Val and Geronimo were sprawled in the sand wrapped in a fierce embrace, looking for all the world like one huge black spider.

Helen took his hand and they strolled along the water's edge chatting like old friends, comfortable in each other's company. He discovered that she was camping near her parents' caravan, having hitchhiked from Newcastle with Val as there was no room in the family car; that she and Val had been friends since childhood, and that her parents did not trust them to go camping on their own. By the time they returned to their friends, Terry's jeans were dry and they'd provided each other with an exhaustive run down on their past lives and hopes and fears for the future.

The girls insisted on walking back alone so they arranged to meet again that night. It was a pretty safe bet that their excitable friends would by now be barred from the Bamburgh Castle along with anyone looking remotely like them, so they decided to meet in the Black Swan, a smaller, quieter pub.

The boys were in the process of brewing up a cup of coffee on Terry's tiny primus when the Squatters returned, laden down with an assortment of food. It seemed that Noddy had taken to knocking at the kitchen doors of various small hotels and with grubby paw outstretched uttering the immortal words: "Gis a bira bread Bob". Anxious to be rid of this apparition, the kitchen staff had handed over chicken legs, fish in batter, steak and kidney pie and all manner of other goodies.

Hank took charge of fire lighting duties and found that the National Trust "No Camping" sign made excellent kindling and with the addition of a plentiful supply of drift wood he soon had a roaring blaze. When the fire died down they cooked up the mélange of assorted food, making Terry glad he had already eaten.

The weather was so hot that even the Squatters acknowledged the fact and the afternoon was spent in a spot of naked bathing and general horseplay. Hank's dog Willy had never known life outside the dirty back lanes of Gateshead and was now revelling in life with his new found friends, running in and out of the sea and chasing the sticks they threw in an ecstasy of excitement.

They headed into town that night looking cleaner than usual, the combination of sea and sun having imparted a certain pinkness to their usually pallid complexions.

Terry and Geronimo met the girls in the Black Swan and they suffered the usual vulgar badinage from the rest of the crowd with equanimity, at least they had a woman. Although she had never met him, Val knew of Hank by reputation. The aspect of his reputation she was most interested in was the rumoured size of his Willie and she was not referring to his faithful dog. During the course of the evening, as she became more emboldened by drink, she began to make reference to the legendary member, claiming that she could not believe he was really Hank. Eventually Hank had heard enough. He stood up and zipped down his fly - he was never one for wearing underpants - exposing an appendage that caused Val to blanch. "Ahm Hank", he bellowed and with that proceeded to dip the offensive weapon into his beer. "Ahm away to the bog, neebody's ganna drink me beer," he sneered.

With that, he zipped up his fly and swaggered off, leaving the assembled company silent for a few seconds before the vulgar remarks began. Of course, this incident caused them to be barred from the pub but, as it was almost closing time, they were not too concerned. So, as they disgorged from the pub, still without any female company, the lads decided to go to the village dance. Against his better judgement, and with some encouragement from Helen, Terry joined them and duly handed over 2/6d each to have his and her hands stamped with indelible dye.

Dances by this time had succumbed to the disco and the appalling local bands no longer held sway, so at least there was some improvement in the music.

What Terry had forgotten was that being with a woman when the local Neanderthals were without one was tantamount to asking for a fight, and it was not long before he was being picked on. He was just trying to think of some means of talking his way out of it when the Frankies homed in on him. This was a perfect opportunity for them to get involved in a fight without having to start it themselves.

Within seconds a battle was raging and the Frankies were winning. Although young fishermen and farmers are, by nature of their jobs, strong and hard, they are no match for vicious city boys who have been fighting since they could walk. However, more locals were joining in and sheer weight of numbers was beginning to take its toll. That's when Big Alex and Co. decided to even things up.

The whole dance floor erupted and even the plucky D.J. - who up until then had kept the music going - began to pack up his records. Unfortunately, the old village hall was made of wood, the end wall of which was beginning to crumble and had been temporarily repaired. As the fighting grew fiercer and moved to that end, the wall began to give way. Suddenly it collapsed and the brawling bodies streamed out into the open air, still fighting. The Squatters, realising that the police would soon be on their way, melted into the night. Terry got out of it with little more than a black eye and a couple of bruised ribs and decided to make his escape. He walked Helen back to the caravan park. She, insisted on leaving him at the gate but made arrangements to hitchhike back with him the next day, feeling sure that Val and Geronimo would be doing the same.

The following afternoon he was waiting on the little stone bridge on the road out of Seahouses where they had arranged to meet. He felt apprehensive, perhaps she would not turn up, but he had no need to worry. He saw her striding along the road towards him, rucksack on both shoulders, long hair caressed by the warm sea breeze, smiling her wonderful mischievous smile and his heart filled with gladness. They set off together, sticking out their thumbs at the occasional passing car, but mainly just enjoying the walk.

Walking seems conducive to talking and Terry was delighted with Helen's conversation, she was an intelligent well read girl with strongly held opinions and a brilliant sense of humour. On and on they wandered enjoying the countryside and the warmth of the weather but mainly taking pleasure in each other's company.

They passed through Beadnell and took the road that led inland towards Alnwick. After a few more miles an old Morris Oxford ground to a halt and the driver offered them a lift to Morpeth. Another lift on a farm lorry dropped them off at what seemed to Helen to be the middle of nowhere, but Terry knew where he was. This was near his old home, he'd roamed these fields and woods as a child.

"Come on," he said, climbing an old stone wall, "there's a stream near here, let's get the primus out and have a brew."

They crossed a field, then entered a dense wood. He led the way until he found what he was looking for, a tiny clearing in the middle of a thicket of young beech trees with a stream dissecting one corner. "These trees have grown a bit, this used to be my own personal hiding place when I was a kid" he explained, "no one else knows about it". He assembled the tiny stove and poured methylated spirits into the reservoir, and taking out a box of Puck matches, he ignited the blue fluid. Once he was satisfied that the appropriate temperature had been achieved, he began pumping through the paraffin which vaporised and produced a roaring blue and white flame of intense heat. Filling his billy-can, he set it to boil while they spread out their sleeping bags.

Soon they were drinking coffee and eating sandwiches, courtesy of

Helen's mum, who had made them up with the fond notion that they would be eaten by the two girls. They lolled in the sun luxuriating in the sensuous warmth, enjoying the food and drink with taste buds made sensitive by the fresh air and recent exercise.

When the meal was over Helen removed her hiking boots and addressed Terry with a winsome smile. "Well, this is just wonderful, I don't care what you think of me but I want this sun on every part of me." He watched while she removed her socks, jeans and blouse, thinking himself fortunate to see her in her underwear, but she did not stop there. She removed her bra and wriggling out of her panties lay prone on the sleeping bag, eyes closed to the sun.

"So you really mean every part of you" Terry almost whimpered, trying his best to make his voice sound normal.

He felt that this was a day he would remember for the rest of his life, so, moving slowly, he removed his own clothes and lay reverently gazing at her beauty, determined to enjoy every second of this experience. The sun beat down on their naked bodies and he could see tiny jewels of perspiration forming above her top lip. He tasted the salt when he kissed her warm, pliant mouth. The air was filled with the drowsy hum of insects interspersed with birdsong, then, increasingly, with Helen's low moans.

He was surprised that someone so apparently sophisticated seemed unconcerned about contraception but he was doing enough worrying for them both, so much so that when the time of climax came, he leapt clear with such alacrity that he inadvertently ejaculated into the upturned cup of her discarded bra. He looked towards her with a pained embarrassed grin. She smiled back a languid smile. "Good shot, Terry, you've just won yourself a goldfish!".

They both laughed hysterically while he cleaned up the sullied garment, then he silenced her laughter with his kisses and they lay together, young limbs entwined, warm, secure and fulfilled, the natural sounds of the woods lulling them to sleep.

As they dozed, a column of tiny black ants attracted by the smell of bacon grease on unwashed mess tins, marched determinedly into the open mouth of Terry's recumbent rucksack.

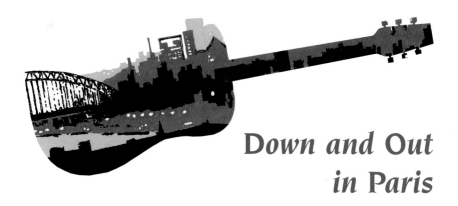

Down and Out
in Paris

From that day on, Terry and Helen were a couple. She fitted into his life and accepted his friends as they welcomed her. Although she still maintained her own companions and went her own way, as lovers they were totally committed to each other.

Of all the crowd, Helen was particularly friendly with Eric's girlfriend, Doreen Caulker and the four of them often went out together, particularly to indulge Eric's taste for obscure art movies. Quiet midweek evenings would often find them at the Pavilion cinema on Westgate Road - once a theatre and now returned to its original use. At that time "The Pav" had a policy of combining obscure foreign films with hearty naturist movies featuring athletic looking nude blonde girls with large breasts and no pubic hair who cavorted in various sports with large hairy naked men filmed only from the waist up or from behind. Together, they saw a great many films in grainy monochrome, including the Jacques Tati classic "Monsieur Hulot's Holiday" and the experimental piece "Shadows", directed by, and featuring John Cassavetes, all hand held cameras and unscripted dialogue.

One film that had a profound effect on the whole crowd was "Jazz On A Summers Day" filmed at the 1958 Newport Jazz Festival. The opening credits alone, featuring Bob Brookmeyer, Jimmy Giuffre and Jim Hall playing "Train And The River", while the camera intercut with shots of the Newport yacht race, is a classic in its own right. No doubt the film had an effect on music fans all over the world and could be said to have been the catalyst that led to the huge festivals that are so common today.

One European festival already well established in 1960 was the Antibes Jazz Festival in the South of France and that year, who should be headlining but Eric's first great influence, Ray Charles. Tickets could be had through the Melody Maker and the whole crowd wanted to go but only Eric, Johnny and Terry were determined enough to rake together the money. They put their cash together and sent off a postal order for three tickets, then set about finding out how to get there.

Somewhere in their communal consciousness they had a vague notion that they could hitch-hike but it soon became apparent that this was impracticable. Luckily, they knew a couple of girls who worked in the travel agent business and so a route was planned.

Alex & Red in Paris, surrealism personified

They would take the train to London on a Friday night, then catch an early bus on Saturday morning down to a tiny airport near Lydd in Kent. A twenty minute flight across the channel would take them to Le Touquet in Normandy where they could take a train which would have them in Paris in about one and a half hours.

Eric, whose connection with Alex went back to his school days, had been to Paris the year before with The Squatters and had found accommodation at a youth hostel owned by the French Communist Party. This was situated in the suburbs of Paris at a place called Malekoff and could be reached by taking the Metro to Port d'Orleans then boarding a local bus for the final short stretch to the hostel.

When the date of departure finally arrived they set off in the afternoon, with rucksacks on their backs, carrying a crate of brown ale between them, to save buying beer on the train. Arriving at King's Cross Station about 7 p.m. they dived straight into the first pub to plan their next move. Luckily, the bus was due to leave next morning from outside Paddington station which they knew was just around the corner. There was only one place to go if you had an evening to spend in London, Ronnie Scott's Jazz Club. Negotiating their way around the tube system took some time but they finally arrived at the club and of course were refused entry, which was just as well because they could not afford the admission charge.

So they explored the London pubs, sticking - like true Geordie chauvinists - to the Youngers' pubs where they drank half bottles of Newcastle Brown in dark brown bottles rather than drink the local brew which they considered to be piss. It was only when the pubs disgorged the last drinkers onto the pavements that they considered the problem of where to sleep. "Wi'll kip in the waiting room at Paddington Station" suggested Eric.

"Excellent idea" slurred Johnny, "handy for the bus, wash and brush up, breakfast in the station buffet, luxury!"

"Then off to Paris in the morning" enthused Terry.

Linking arms they set off for the nearest tube station singing "I love Paris In The Springtime" in what they considered to be perfect three part harmony.

Having found a space among the dossers in the Paddington waiting room, they drifted off to sleep, only to have their slumbers interrupted by the railway police - similar to the regular police but stupider and more vindictive - who turfed out everyone without a valid ticket. The three sleepy boys staggered out into the night, wandered around until they found a railed off city square, climbed the railings, crawled into their sleeping bags and were soon asleep among the shrubbery.

The next morning found them on the coach to Lydd having their needs ministered to by an attractive young hostess who appeared to find their youth and general scruffiness a refreshing change from the general cavalry twills, twin set and pearls types who usually did this route. She made them promise to give her a full report of their adventures at the Antibes Jazz Festival on the return trip.

A twenty minute flight in an ancient turbo prop took them to Le Touquet and they were soon boarding the train for Paris clutching bottles of duty free cognac, something they had never drunk, but which seemed appropriate.

Even though they'd been in the country less than an hour all three had noticed that France smelled different. The combination of red wine, coffee, garlic and Gauloises seemed to permeate the very air they breathed, it certainly permeated the toilets. French piss gave off a particularly lethal odour. This was even more apparent once they were on the streets of Paris: the colourful pissoires - as seen on so many impressionist paintings and on picture postcards of the capital - were still in use and exuded their own distinctive whiff.

The boys wandered down streets so utterly like their preconceived ideas of Paris that they felt as if they were on the set of a film. Spotting the elaborate cast iron portals of a Metro station they descended into the Paris underground and were enchanted by the sight and sounds of a variety of buskers, something unknown on the London underground at that time. The Metro maps were easy to follow and in less than twenty minutes they surfaced at Port d'Orleans.

Another aspect of Paris, common in so many of the subtitled French films they had watched back home, were the ancient green single-decker buses. They were designed with a platform at the rear, open to the weather, where most people seemed to prefer to ride, even though there were vacant seats inside. Luck was on their side, they flagged down a bus whose destination board showed Malekof and completed the last leg of their journey on the rear platform, watching the pageant of the city streets in a dreamlike state.

Malekof Youth Hostel turned out to be a run-down old sports stadium whose indoor basket ball hall had been partitioned off into makeshift dormitories and whose rugby pitch was now a camp site. There was a shower and toilet block, a kitchen with cooking and washing up facilities and precious little else. The kitchen, situated

Johnny & Terry in Paris

160

on a large balcony overlooking the defunct race track, contained rows of trestle tables and forms and was open to the weather. This proved to be the main meeting place and was usually thronged with people eating, drinking, reading, writing or deep in conversation. After checking in and being shown their room - a dormitory containing six beds - they made for the kitchen and were made welcome by the residents.

A great many nationalities were using the place including Spanish, Japanese, Dutch, German and Swedish. There were no other English although most of them seemed to be able to speak it and were using it as a common language. They were befriended by a young Dutchman with long hair and a wispy beard who called himself Harry. He wished to be a writer and had read many English books, his favourite being Sillitoe's "Saturday Night And Sunday Morning". Once he realised that the boys were northern and working class he was avid for stories of the gritty north. He was delighted when, before they would settle down for a chat, they enquired about the drink situation and he showed them the way to a nearby shop which sold red wine at ridiculously low prices. While there, they purchased bread and cheese, also eggs, sugar and coffee for the morning.

Back at the hostel they had their first drink of red wine. The taste was something of a shock at first but with the aid of the bread and cheese they persevered and as the alcohol kicked in, so their taste buds relished the new flavour. Harry plied them with questions about the North and they obliged with lurid tales about Newcastle, Gateshead and life on the road with the Squatters. The supply of red wine was running low so Johnny decided to make coffee and broach his duty free cognac. Eric and Terry of course had to follow suit, soon everyone in the kitchen was drinking coffee and cognac.

During the course of their interrogation, Harry had elicited the information that they were in a band so he now called for a song. Eric was quick to oblige and the sound of "Roll Over Beethoven" echoed round the darkened stadium. More wine, more brandy and many more songs later, the boys finished off the evening with an exhibition of table dancing á la The Squatters before staggering off to their respective camp beds.

The next morning, Terry awoke to find his vision impaired by a red mist. Somewhere in the distance he could hear water sloshing rhythmically. This turned out to be the sound of a mop being plied by a large French lady unconcernedly cleaning round their beds while they slept. With some difficulty he focused on his watch. It was half past ten. He turned his gaze on his sleeping companions whose pallid complexions told the story of last night's excesses. He groaned weakly and went back to sleep. By the afternoon, they had recovered enough to make it to the kitchen, where their new friend Harry gave them coffee and fresh baked bread, seeming to consider their hangovers as a romantic manifestation of their hardbitten Northerness, whereas they considered their suffering to be a product of their own stupidity - until the next time!

After a shower and more food they felt fit enough to set off for the Gare Du Nord station to make enquiries on how to get to Antibes, the festival being in three days' time. The Gauloise-smoking gentleman at the enquiries desk spoke perfect English and was able to inform them of all available trains and the price of the tickets. It was only then that these three innocents realised that France is an appreciably larger country than Britain. At a time when the return fare from Newcastle to London was seven pounds, after doing the conversion from francs they realised that it would cost them seventeen pounds each to get to Antibes. Terry had exactly seventeen pounds left, Johnny and Eric had slightly less.

They walked away from the station with a dejected air, the prospect of seeing Ray Charles receding with every step. "Seventeen fuckin quid" spluttered Eric, "thas only one thing for it, w'ill have ti hitch it."

"It's in the south of France" said Johnny, "God knows how many hundred miles."

"Wi couldn't split up" added Terry, "wi'd just get separated, and nobody's ganna pick three up."

They made their way back to Malekof discussing various courses of action but knowing in their hearts that they were never going to make it.

As they walked down the street approaching the stadium they passed a typical French bar with blue wooden shutters and a few small round tables and high backed chairs out on the pavement. The door was open and the sound of music drifted out onto the street. They recognised it immediately, the opening bars of "The Night Time Is The Right Time" by Ray Charles. Without saying a word they walked into the bar. Johnny and Eric made straight for the juke box, while Terry headed for the highly polished copper counter and ordered three beers. The juke box proved to contain a wealth of material, mostly American rhythm-&-blues or rock-&-roll, with a preponderance of Ray Charles' records.

Five minutes later they were sitting round a table drinking the wonderful pale golden beer of Alsace and searching their pockets for suitable coins for the machine. Perhaps things weren't so bad after all. The tables nearest the juke box were occupied by a group of French teenagers who watched these newcomers with interest, seeming to take especial notice of their choice of music. The group consisted of three boys and three girls. Two of the boys were dark-haired and handsome with typically Gallic features, the other was blonde with rugged good looks and more Scandinavian than French.

Obviously, Terry and the boys were more interested in the young ladies in the party. They had already noticed that French women of whatever age seemed, by and large, to have an innate ability to look chic in the simplest of clothes, these girls personified that flair. The only one wearing make-up was blonde with discreetly bouffant hair, pale pink lipstick and the looks of a young Brigette Bardot. A second blonde wore her hair in a short tousled boyish style: her suntanned face had just enough freckles to look cute. By contrast, the other girl was very dark with black shoulder-length hair, her huge brown eyes framed by long lashes devoid of mascara.

A couple of beers and several visits to the juke box later, a mutual admiration for Ray Charles bridged the language barrier and drew the French and British teenagers together. They were soon deep in conversation using a sort of pidgin Franglaise covering the topics of music, movies, books and motor bikes. In fact, the blonde boy Gerard spoke quite good English and the two dark haired boys Bernard and Roger could speak a little. Of the girls, the young Brigette, real name Annique, spoke none and her blonde friend Marie could make herself understood. The third girl, dark haired, enigmatic Phillipa did not say enough for them to form an opinion of her linguistic abilities though her dark eyes spoke volumes.

At first, the boys assumed that they were talking to three couples but, as the evening progressed, it was explained that the boys were either brother or cousin to the girls and were in fact acting as chaperons. At that time in France, girls who went out without a chaperon were not considered to be decent and were a target for

French, English & Swedish on the roof at Malekof

wagging tongues. This piece of information greatly heartened the three young Geordies, provoking them to fantasies of love, lust and conquest that would never be fulfilled. They left the little bar that night full of beer and bonhomie promising to see their new found friends the following evening.

Back at the hostel Harry was still up, so more red wine had to be drunk while the days events were dissected. Much to the Dutchman's delight they decided to stay at the hostel and spend the rest of their holiday exploring Paris, as long as the money didn't run out. Harry was staying for a few months and was on a very tight budget so he was unable to accompany them, but the next day they became acquainted with two Swedish boys who were more than happy to do so. Chris and George were typically Swedish in appearance, clean cut with short blond hair but much more demonstrative than their compatriots. That night, the boys introduced them to the local bar and taught them how to drink beer in rounds, something neither they nor the French boys were used to.

So their days took on some kind of structure. Mornings, rise late and have a prolonged breakfast, spend the afternoons sightseeing in Paris sometimes accompanied by Bernard who would show them where to buy a cheap meal, fill the evenings in the little bar drinking beer, playing the juke box, talking and eating Madame's hard boiled eggs always for sale in a basket on the counter. The Swedes were anxious to see Paris at night so the boys agreed to join them, making sure they took some cheap red wine as the prices in the centre were exorbitant. They wandered the streets of this wonderful, vibrant city together, drinking in the sights and the sounds and also drinking the red wine which made the whole experience even more exhilarating.

Eventually they found themselves at the Place Pigalle, home of the Folies Bergeres and various other slightly less salubrious establishments. They were amazed to find a plethora of prostitutes blatantly plying their wares in full view of the passing gendarmes. Although Terry had seen a few tarts in Newcastle and observed a

*Eric samples
the red wine*

higher class variety in London's Soho, these beautiful French ladies
of the night were a revelation. They were so glamorous that they
looked like film stars to these young innocents and the idea that
anyone could have sex with them just by paying over money
seemed beyond belief. They parked themselves on a bench and
passed the bottles round and watched the theatre of the street
with interest. If they had harboured any doubts as to the profession
of these girls it was soon dispelled as they watched them barter
with their clients then disappear into a sleazy hotel, returning in
what seemed like a very short time. George and Chris seemed very
interested in what was on offer and as they had no shortage of
money even went as far as to ask "combien?" only turning it into a
joke when confronted by jeers from their new found friends.

When the wine ran out, they headed back towards the Metro calling
in on a few bars on the way. By now they were truly pissed and the
boys decided to introduce the two Swedes to the old squatters'
trick of making your way along the street on the roofs of parked

cars. The Swedes took to this activity with alacrity, only coming to a halt when George stepped on a soft top. In a city where the police are notoriously vicious and carry guns, they were taking a terrible chance, but the god that preserves drunks was on duty again that night and no gendarme put on an appearance.

This visit to the city at night was so exhilarating that they went back again and again, until one night when walking down by the banks of the Seine, Eric, Johnny and Terry were set upon by a group of Algerian youths. Being drunk and in a foreign land, coupled with the fact that they now considered themselves to be hard Northerners, seemed to give them confidence and they were quick to retaliate, swinging in to action like the Squatters on a Saturday night. Perhaps the antagonists were used to soft targets. After a brief struggle they disappeared into the night leaving the boys flushed with triumph. However, their elation was somewhat diminished when they realised that Johnny's watch had been neatly removed from his wrist in the fracas.

This incident, and the fact that money was running low, convinced them to spend the rest of the holiday in and around Port d'Orleans, especially in the vicinity of their neighbourhood bar and the beautiful French girls, who remained permanently unattainable. This fact, and the constant stimulation of seeing so many desirable prostitutes, was having a devastating effect on Terry's libido. He began to miss Helen more and more even to the point of imagining himself in love and a part of him began to pine for home.

Fate was soon to step in and fulfil this desire. One night after a particularly raucous evening culminating in mass singing in the hostel kitchen, the three boys staggered off to bed, giggling, Eric still swigging a bottle of red wine. They had stripped down to their underpants and were ready to crawl into bed when Terry reached out drunkenly for the bottle. "Haway man, diffint hog it all" he slurred.

As the transfer of the bottle took place, red wine somehow sloshed over Eric's already wine stained tee shirt lying crumpled on his bed.

Eric grabbed the bottle back. "Yi fuckin clumsy bastard" he shouted, showing his talent for the cutting aphorism.

With that, he poured red wine over Terry's sleeping bag. They were soon rolling on the floor in a clinch while Johnny lay on his bed smoking a Gitane and watching with interest. A clean-living Japanese boy had the misfortune to share their dormitory. Usually taciturn he now spoke forth. "If you have argument, please take it outside, you disturb my sleep."

The boys already had him figured as some kind of martial arts expert so they decided to take his advice and staggered off into the night. They lurched into the middle of the rugby pitch cum camp site and squared up to each other. After a great deal of ineffectual flailing, Eric connected with a crack to Terry's jaw which floored him. Unfortunately for Eric the crack was the sound of his thumb breaking and he too ended up on the ground writhing in pain. After lying there for some time contemplating their folly and becoming aware of their unclad bodies they picked themselves up and helped each other back to the warmth of the dorm.

The Japanese boy proved sympathetic and produced bandages to bind up Eric's thumb which was swelling rapidly. The next day they sought out the local doctor who rebound the digit, pronouncing it well and truly broken and in need of hospital treatment. Although the doctor waived his fee, he warned them that the necessary treatment would be expensive in France and advised a return to Britain and the highly lauded National Health Service.

They only had a couple of days left and money was running short so, with Bernards help, they sought out the Paris office of their travel company and arranged to travel back the next day. Midmorning on the morrow found them sprawling against their rucksacks in the Gare du Nord, while Bernard, Chris and George photographed them in all their dishevelled glory, the two tidy Swedes taking particular delight in their scruffiness. They all exchanged addresses and promised to keep in touch but they did not expect ever to see each other again.

For Terry this would turn out to be true, but in four year's time Johnny and Eric were destined to meet up with Bernard under entirely different circumstances. He would be driving them around Paris in his Citroen 2CV after seeing them play to a packed house at the Paris Olympia as part of a chart topping group called The Animals. Chris and George would also meet them again as part of a select few invited back stage for drinks after a sell-out concert at Stockholm's City Hall.

The Le Touquet train drew in and they piled on board and claimed a seat, then proceeded to hang out of the window waving at their friends. Suddenly struck by a sense of loss, Terry returned to his seat and gazed determinedly out of the window, choking back his tears. The other two returned and all three were quiet for a while, lost in their own personal reveries until Eric spoke up. "Ah couldn't half fancy a pint of Exhibition and a Dickmans pork pie"

"Yea" the other two chorused. The mood changed. They were looking forward to going home, to telling the tale, boasting about their experiences and most of all making love to their respective girl friends.

The journey home was uneventful, and about eight o'clock that evening their train wheezed to a halt in Newcastle Central Station. They stepped back into their old life breathing in the cold northern air and seeing the old place in a new light. Imbued with a feeling of elation and love for their home town, they walked straight across the road to the Victoria and Comet - the only pub in town still with sawdust on the floor - and downed three pints of Newcastle Exhibition.

Thirst quenched, they went their separate ways arranging to meet the following night in Simpsons. They still had the weekend ahead of them.

The first thing Terry did the next day was to get in touch with Helen where she worked and persuade her to stay out all night. She duly arrived at Simpsons with her rucksack, off camping as far as her parents were concerned. It was early, no one else had arrived. He took her off to the last booth at the end of the long room. She wore a soft white blouse with a collar of Broderie Anglaise, over which her dark auburn hair flowed like silk. He cupped her lovely face in his hands and kissed her eyes, her cheeks, her mouth. "I've missed you. Helen, I've missed you so very much."

She snuggled in to his chest. "And I've missed you. Next time we'll go together, but now, why not tell me all about it?"

Their solitude was short lived - they could hear voices at the bar, the rest of the crowd were filtering in. Before too long they were surrounded by people and Eric was in full flow, ably abetted by Terry and Johnny. The evening was theirs and they took advantage of the fact, spinning stories like magic webs of fantasy, turning every tale into an epic. Eric was still in full flow when Helen and Terry made a discreet exit, heading for East Parade and a night of love making of such intensity that the memory would always stay with him.

The next morning they were propped up in the big old brass bed sipping coffee from big earthenware mugs. The shutters were open, affording an eye level view of the back yard and the morning sun was at a height where it illuminated the whole room, warming the bright coloured blanket serving as a bed cover and accentuating the stark black and white of the Aubrey Beardsley print on the chimney breast. Miles Davis's "Birth Of The Cool" poured forth from the old Dansette, life felt good. Terry had never told anyone he loved them before. He had heard the words used so often at the cinema: somehow the idea of uttering them in a Geordie accent did not ring true.

Such doubts were not occupying his mind at that moment as he took Helen's empty cup and kissed her warm lips still tasting of coffee. "Thanks for last night" he whispered, turning his attention to the softness of her neck, "I love you, Helen."

She gently disengaged him from the folds of her hair and cupping his face in her hands, looked deep into his eyes. "Hold on, Molloy,

I know you missed me but don't say that unless you're sure, please, you've got to be sure."

He pulled her to his chest, adjusting her long hair and stroking the gleaming strands. Out in the yard he could see a squabbling gang of sparrows fighting over a chicken carcase, no doubt deposited there by Mrs Rickets. He pulled the blanket up over them and held her very tight, but he did not say it again.

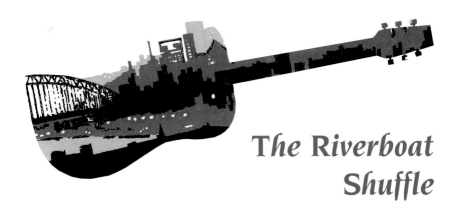

The Riverboat Shuffle

In their absence, The Squatters had been improving on their notoriety to the point where some of their exploits - wildly exaggerated - had been reported in The Newcastle Evening Chronicle. This of course only served to encourage them to greater excesses. A trip to The Old George gave them the information that the destination for the following weekend was Hexham, so Johnny Eric and Terry decided to get back on the road.

The only problem was that one of the Frankies was having a twenty first birthday party. He'd booked a room in the Globe in Gateshead and the band were invited to play. Animal decreed that they could still go squatting, they could simply leave their bindles in the station left luggage office and catch the last train to Hexham after the party. On hearing of the venue for the gig Jeff Hedley refused to take his precious tenor anywhere near the Globe, so they would have to manage without a tenor. After some reflection they decided it might be better if Danny and Pat gave it a miss. The rougher elements of Gateshead at that time were not renowned for their tolerance of other races. A Sikh bus conductor, the first to have worked the Gateshead route had recently been thrown off a moving bus and was only saved from serious injury by his turban. So the band would consist of Eric on vocals - the pub did have a mike-

SCOURGE OF THE NORTH EAST COAST

Police spokesman voices concern over "Wild Ones" - Arrests made across the coast

Pricey on piano and Johnny on very basic drum kit - snare drum and high-hat, as their was no mention of a fee, this would suffice.

The party was on a Friday night, so at opening time 6 p.m. everyone going squatting was in the Victoria and Comet - or Spit and Vomit as it was affectionately referred to - wearing their usual rags and carrying their bindles. Two or three pints later, belongings safely stashed in the station left luggage office, they were on the bus en route to the Globe.

The rest of the crowd were already there. Smartly dressed in suits, with highly polished shoes and clean shining hair, they stood around chatting in a civilised manner. A table of food stood against one wall and one or two older people, obviously family, hovered near it. The band played the first half to everyone's satisfaction and interval time brought the traditional wolfing of the food with the band getting its fair share. Terry was beginning to wish that they had brought the whole band, it was turning into a good night. They kicked off the second half with 'Sweet Little Sixteen' having decided to favour rock and roll rather than rhythm and blues, soon the dance floor was full and the place was rocking.

One or two locals had filtered in from the public bar but no one seemed to mind, until one or two became a crowd, all wearing a sneer, intent on trouble. They'd come to the right place! In a Gateshead minute everything had changed and the place was in an uproar, tables were overturned, glasses broken and bodies flew across the room in a ballet of violence. By some ironic coincidence the band had just broken into the Little Richard song "Rip It Up". As the stage seemed the safest place to be, Terry and Dave Wilson decided that the band needed a little help on the harmonies on this one.

From this vantage point they watched the burly landlord trying to restore order in the way that burly landlords do, that is by throwing everyone outside. The band stopped playing and Johnny stashed his drums under the stage. Now was the time to leave. The fight was still progressing on the pavement and as it was certain that the police had been called, Alex and Animal were marshalling the troops. "Right lads to the station" they roared and suiting the words to the deed they ran across the road to where a double decker bus was just pulling in.

The familiar sound of the bell on a Black Maria stimulated the rest of the crowd, no one wished to be arrested by the Gateshead coppers as their unconventional way of dealing with trouble makers was liable to leave a person feeling rather sore. The bus was pulling out with only Alex and Animal on board. They stood on the platform and managed to haul everyone in as the bus gradually gathered momentum. Of course, they could easily have pressed the bell and stopped the vehicle but that lacked style and anyway every second counted.

Just time to grab a few bottles at the Spit and Vomit and then on to the station and the last train to Hexham. Terry was glad to be out of the city and as the train gathered speed and the suburbs turned to countryside he observed the tension leaving the faces of his friends. They sprawled out on the seats, relaxed and content, looking forward to their weekend in the country, all except Pricey who was wearing his city clothes and a bewildered expression. Somehow, his plans for the weekend had been changed.

By the time they arrived at Hexham the streets were empty and their footsteps echoed on the damp streets . They were heading for a quarry on the edge of town where they expected to find a few of the crowd who had not deigned to attend the party. They passed a flashing plastic Belisha beacon, a new innovation replacing the old solid painted variety introduced by Hoare Belisha in the twenties.

Dave Wilson, who had consumed more than his usual quota of brown ale, decided that it was winking at him and he decided to teach it a lesson. He bounded over and gave the offending spheroid a mighty punch whereupon it flew off, bounced down the road and was quickly adopted as a football by Noddy and Spud.

Unluckily for Dave the incident had been observed by a young policeman standing in a shop doorway, enjoying the illegal pleasures of nicotine after a fairly uneventful evening. The young copper stepped into view with some trepidation. In those days you could only summon help by blowing your whistle and he knew there was no one within whistling distance. But he need not have worried, although outlandish in appearance this crowd seemed distinctly non-threatening.

He made Dave replace the orange football and, after giving him a good telling-off, demanded his name and address. Like most city kids, Dave was inured to verbal warnings by the police and he fell back on a well tested ploy. In the Walker area of Newcastle there was a block of flats called The Dwellings designed by some well-meaning architect to re-house people from the slums. The place was surrounded by railings and was so soulless and prison-like that it affected the behaviour of the inhabitants, many of whom ended up in prison. The city council in its wisdom moved problem families there and soon it became a no-go area for the police. So, if you were stopped by the police in Newcastle and claimed to come from Walker Dwellings, chances were they wouldn't want the hassle of visiting your parents and would let you go. Dave automatically gave a false name with E. block as an address and they all went on their way.

They were just about to take the Allendale road out of town when a Black Maria screamed to a halt next to them and out jumped a sergeant - it was the laughing policeman - and a young constable, along with a couple of other burly coppers." When one of my lads asks for your address" said the sergeant," I want the correct address and the correct name. Have you got that?"

With that, they threw a protesting Dave into the back of the van and sped off. "Well, at least he'll ger a bed for the night" said Hank.

"Aye, and a good breakfast" added Red.

So, with poor Wilson consigned to his fate, they went on their way out of town along the unlit road. It was a boring journey until they came upon a red and white workman's hut surrounded by red lamps. Animal stepped inside and, lifting the tent up bodily set off up the road, intoning "I'm a tortoise, ah carry me home on me back". Some picked up the lamps, while the rest discovered picks and shovels and slinging them over their shoulders marched off up the road singing, "Hi, Ho, Hi, Ho, its off to work we go". Eric, being an artist, picked up a pot of red lead and a brush in case an opportunity for some graffiti presented itself.

When the time came to leave the road, the tent was abandoned and they set off across the fields, eventually coming to a thicket of beech saplings. Through the trees they could see a fire flickering: they had reached the quarry. The Chambers' brothers, Davey Crockett, Jean and Paula were already there, sitting round the fire drinking beer and cooking sausages. This was the time that Terry liked best, when they were alone together, away from the rest of civilisation, at one with the trees and plants, close to the earth, staring into the ancient primeval force of the fire. When the cooking was done they fed the primeval force a bit more wood, making the flames grow higher, illuminating and casting shadows on the quarry walls.

Eric decided it was time to utilise his paint brush and set to work on the bare rock, spilling a great deal of paint in the process. After a while he gave up in disgust, appalled by his lack of co-ordination and crawled fully clothed into his sleeping bag. Clutching a bottle of beer in his paint spattered hand he was content to gaze into the fire with the rest joining in the conversation as the world was put to rights.

Alex and Animal had read extensively on the exploits of the French Voyagers who had opened up the unexplored regions of Canada, and the Mountain Men who roamed the Appalachian mountains of America and they discoursed at length about their exploits. This was why they loved the wilder, more remote places, just for the weekend, they too could be Mountain Men or Voyagers. Not for the first time it occurred to Terry that they had been born into the wrong time.

Gradually everyone was slipping away. Eric dozed off, bottle in hand, and Johnny was already snoring peacefully. Terry gave up his sleeping bag to Pricey and after some special pleading managed to crawl in with Paula. The fire was dying down and a frost was forming. It would be cold in the morning.

The next morning, after a leisurely breakfast, Terry persuaded the loquacious Spud to accompany him to the police station on a mercy mission to try to secure Dave's release without having to suffer the usual punishment of detention until the pubs closed. Luckily, the laughing policeman was not on duty and on being told that they were leaving town the desk sergeant agreed to Dave's release, with dire warnings against any future misdemeanours. Such was the system of justice administered by the Hexham police at that time, it required no paperwork and was effective.

So it was off to the Carts Bog Inn with Pricey in tow. As soon as the landlord spotted Alan, he handed over the keys to the piano. As long as there was music there seemed to be less boisterous behaviour and he enjoyed it as much as anyone. Pricey could play in any style and was happy to accompany anyone who felt like singing their favourite song. Alex would usually call for jazz and he would oblige with a bit of Brubeck, Monk, or even Jelly Roll Morton. But usually the place did not start jumping until Eric got up and belted out some good old rhythm and blues. Apart from Wednesday nights at the New Orleans the band was not playing many gigs, so Johnny, Eric and Alan found themselves available for more weekends in the country.

This was considered by the Squatters to be a satisfactory state of affairs as they considered the music to be their own. A few weeks later they were all in Hexham once again, congregated in the Railway Tavern which had a decent piano. This was a convenient spot, as they had taken to sleeping in the greenhouses of an abandoned nursery situated close by, the wood-yard having been abandoned as a resting place when Geronimo woke to find a large rat eating the Brylcream on his hair.

Among the crowd that weekend were three likely lads: Dougie Robson, Bob Wilson and Alan Simpson. These three were always on

Likely lads on the pull

the hunt for talent so, although they wore filthy torn combat jackets, they tended to wear smarter clothes underneath so that should the occasion demand they could they could abandon their outer skin and make themselves presentable.

On this occasion they planned to visit the local dance hall as singer Johnny Gentle was appearing and was bound to attract a good proportion of females. Johnny Gentle was the latest manifestation from the stable of impresario Larry Parnes, who managed a string of fifties' stars with similar names. Adam Faith, Billy Fury, Marty Wilde and Vince Eager were among the most popular, but there were many more who didn't make it and Johnny Gentle was destined to be one of them.

Once they had imbibed enough drink, the rest of the crowd decided that they too were in a dancing mood so they set off for the town hall. Thanks to Alex's powers of persuasion they managed to gain admittance, despite their disreputable appearance, and were just in time to catch the lacklustre end of the singer's first spot.

The band left the stage to muted applause, leaving it bare apart from a grand piano and a gleaming set of drums. "Haway lads" said Animal, "it's your turn next". Emboldened by drink and encouraged by the rest of The Squatters, Johnny, Eric and Pricey took to the stage. Eric switched on the mike and launched into an old Gene Vincent number called "Say Momma" with Pricey belting the keys of the grand piano with consummate skill and maximum volume, while Johnny made full use of the huge drum kit.

The effect on the crowd was immediate and dramatic. Terry and Paula took to the floor first, followed by Davie Phipps and Irene. As if in a scene from a corny rock & roll movie the locals all joined in and soon the floor was packed with bopping bodies. It was no surprise when Johnny Gentle's band appeared from the dressing room, along with a couple of mean looking bouncers, to put a stop to the proceedings, only to find themselves confronted by a ragged bunch of wild looking people.

After a rather heated discussion it was agreed that the boys could continue playing the interval, with the proviso that they played only three more songs. The three songs stretched into a 45 minute spot. For once the local tearaways were on the side of the Squatters, so the bouncers and dance organisers took a pragmatic approach and let them carry on. It was only respect for fellow musicians that finally prompted the three boys to leave the stage, to enthusiastic shouts for more from the audience.

Johnny Gentle did not realise it, but this was a prophetic moment for himself and the many established ballad singers and Elvis look-alikes who had dominated the charts for so long. There was a desire for change among the new generation of music fans and all over the country a spontaneous musical revolution was taking place, that was about to consign Gentle and his ilk into the history books of popular music.

Now that the excitement was over the Squatters could concentrate on the local female talent, although the three erstwhile entertainers received the most attention from the girls. The temporary truce with the locals was over and just to complete the evening of the now distraught Johnny Gentle, the Frankies, true to form, started a battle. As Terry made to leave the place, he reflected that with all this excitement there would be a few knee tremblers around the back alleys of Hexham that night. For himself he noticed a small dark haired girl he remembered having chatted to on several occasions in the past. Avoiding the flying bodies he made his way to her side.

Terry was now in the fifth year of a six year apprenticeship and was earning eight pounds a week - more with overtime - which was considered a good wage at that time. His old school mate, Bill Davidson, still frequented the New Orleans. He was now working in a Building Society and persuaded Terry that he ought to save. As most of his money seemed to be going on booze, he decided to allocate two pounds a week towards some unknown future which he wasted no time in contemplating. So, every Friday he made his way down Clayton Street to the Co-operative Building Society as much to see Bill as to hand over his money, but it would prove to be a sensible move.

He and George Stoves still spent their lunchtimes together, often taking their sandwiches up to Leazes Park. They would take out a boat on the lake and let it drift while they ate and talked, wishing they did not have to go back to work. Although George knew

Terry's mates and often put on an appearance at Simpsons Buffet, or showed up at their parties, he tended to go his own way, so they had more to talk about. He still played guitar and had been in various bands but never seemed to commit himself for long.

In his perambulations around the various pubs and working men's clubs around Heaton, Walker and Wallsend he had seen a great deal of Chas Chandler's band The Kontors and had sat in with them on occasions. Whereas the Kansas City Seven were trying to play the music they loved to a largely unresponsive audience, Chas was determined to succeed and was happy to give the public what they wanted. He had no desire to spend the rest of his life in the shipyards and music was his way out. Always a good organiser, he managed to keep a band together, make them practise and get them gigs, for which they arrived on time and sober.

As the autumnal days grew colder Terry and George's visits to the park grew fewer, but one particularly sunny day they made their way up Leazes Park Road to a tiny shop where they bought stottie cake - a circular loaf of unleavened bread - peculiar to the north east, which could be purchased with a variety of fillings, bacon, sausage, egg, spam, or a combination of all four. Armed with half stotties anointed with brown sauce and with bottles of milk to wash it down, they headed for the park. The Newcastle Breweries was not far away and one of the hazards of the park was a run in with the female brewery workers. They had a fearsome reputation for what would become known as sexual harassment, so, any sign of the distinctive red and brown overalls and the boys would take the opposite direction. On this occasion the coast was clear, in fact the place was deserted and they had the boating lake to themselves.

After eating their stotties and consigning their milk bottles to the deep, they took an oar each and were engaged in breaking the world speed record for rowing boats when Terry spotted a female figure on the shore. She was young, slim and smartly dressed, her red hair was short and her heels were high. She was pushing a pram. It was Hazel.

"Hey, George," said Terry, "see her in the green coat? Shi's a friend of mine, can whi pull alongside ah?"

Without asking any questions he complied and they were soon sculling along the edge of the lake, keeping pace with the pram. Hazel, long practised in ignoring impudent young men, strode on as if they did not exist. Terry exhorted George to greater efforts and they pulled far enough ahead for Terry to leap ashore and change her aloof expression into one of recognition and pleasure.

"So you really were pregnant and now you're pushing a pram like a proper mam."

He desperately wished to say something more profound, but could not find the right words. Hazel did not seem to notice and kissed him warmly on the cheek.

"Ah've been coming up here all Summer, I always thought I might bump into you".

"Whi come up here a lot, me and George. This is George, by the way. George, Hazel."

The recipient of this introduction, having shipped the oars, was now engaged in lighting up a cigarette.

"Pleased to meet yih, pet," he said after taking a deep. Then addressing Terry. "Ah'll just take the boat back, see you later."

With that, he dipped the oars deep into the muddy water and sped off back to the boathouse.

"So what make of baby have yih got?" asked Terry, continuing in crass mode and gazing down into the pram at the sleeping child.

"A girl," she replied, "I've called her Charlotte."

His face softened. "Nice name. Ah see she's got your red hair. Ah'll bet shi'll have lovely green eyes like you as well."

She smile. "She probably will when she's older, they're blue at the moment".

Looking into those green eyes he noticed they were devoid of mascara, in fact other than a trace of lipstick, she wore no make up at all. Her nails, usually long with red nail varnish, were now natural and trimmed short.

"Having a baby must agree with you," he said, taking a seat on a park bench,"you look beautiful."

She put the brake on the pram and sat down beside him.

"Thanks, ah suppose I'm living a healthy life, plenty of long walks and no cigarettes."

They sat close together, without touching, while she told him about her life, her husband's job, his company car and all about the baby. Although he would have loved to entertain her with exaggerated stories of his own recent adventures, he resisted the temptation and was content to listen, plying her with the occasional question, simply enjoying her company. Out of the corner of his eye he could see George, heading for the gates of the park. It was time to go. He kissed her on the mouth, letting his lips linger for a second , then headed after George.

"Ah'll see you soon," he said.

"Yes, I'm often up here, though the weather's changing. It might be spring before!"

"Ah hope not," he replied, breaking into a trot, hoping that George would have the good sense to clock him in.

Winter was indeed approaching and only the hardest of the Squatters were going away for the weekend. Terry and the Simpsons crowd stuck to the routine of Fridays at the Downbeat and Saturdays at the New Orleans which was still the venue for the band's regular Wednesday spot. Mike Jeffries decided he needed live music at the Marimba coffee house, so he offered Pricey and Johnny a residency. They added a bass player and played mainly jazz standards, with Alan playing in a style inspired by the great Oscar Peterson. He was also fond of cocktail bar singer-pianist Buddy Greco and did a passable imitation of his laid-back style. It was not possible to buy a drink at The Marimba without buying a meal, so the crowd took to smuggling in bottles of V.P. wine, a lethal fortified wine guaranteed to get one wrecked and provide a horrendous hangover in the morning.

As the Christmas of 1960 approached, there was little evidence in the music charts that rock and roll had ever existed. Elvis Presley had long ago lost his hard edge, his heavily orchestrated ballad "Its Now Or Never" selling 750,000 copies in the first week of release. This carried him over into January of 1961 and was followed by a lachrymose dirge unearthed from the back catalogues of the Forties called "Are You Lonesome Tonight?"

Meanwhile in Liverpool, The Beatles had their first gig in The Cavern Club, supporting The Bluegenes, later to re-emerge as The Swinging Blue Jeans. Something was stirring in pop music's subculture.

The need for exciting music that could be danced to was always there and traditional jazz fulfilled that role. Despite their interest in rhythm and blues the crowd continued to support the local jazz bands and among The Squatters big Alex was in particular was an avid fan and no mean clarinettist himself. Suddenly the big three of British bands , Chris Barber, Acker Bilk and Kenny Ball began to sell singles, which although never reaching no.1 dominated the higher reaches of the charts. There was a trad boom and following the example set by Acker Bilk with his bowler hat and waistcoat the bands began to wear silly uniforms. Eccentric band leader Pete Deuchar left his regular band, The Vieux Carré, and headed for London to form The Confederates, who wore the appropriate uniform and achieved a modicum of success for a while .

There was even a television programme featuring the music called It's Trad, Dad and as every major city had a fair sprinkling of local bands there was no shortage of talent. If the bands wore uniforms, so did the fans - duffle coats, cord trousers, baggy sweaters, long hair and beards were the norm, although some of the girls did not have beards. Modern jazz fans considered themselves superior to "the traddies" and were considerably better dressed. The boys were clean shaven with short hair and tended towards shirts with button-down collars, short jackets, white macs and winkle-picker shoes. The girls were very smart in a severe clean-cut way, with short hair, tastefully applied make up and the minimum of jewellery. The two camps did not mix and despised each other's taste in music.

Terry's crowd, in contrast, had an eclectic taste in music. And their sartorial style could only be described as raggy chic. As trad fans, one feature of the year's calendar that they always enjoyed were the river boat shuffles. Some jazz buff in the Fifties had read of river boat shuffles taking place on the Mississippi River, consisting of non-stop music and non-stop drinking, so decided to try the same thing on the River Tyne.

It was possible to hire one of the ferries that plied between North and South Shields for a reasonable fee. There was a bar on board and as far as the law was concerned, as soon as the boat cast off from the shore licensing laws did not apply. The crew were happy to take you as far up river as you desired, serving drinks at exorbitant prices all the way and were quite happy to accommodate a band, to create an atmosphere conducive to drinking. The usual route was from the Newcastle quayside up river to Ryton Willows where the passengers disembarked and the band would set up in one of the local pubs. Once closing time was called it was back to the boat and back on the booze until reaching the quayside once more.

One Wednesday night in the Old George, this subject was being discussed by a group of bored midweek drinkers, including Alex, Hank, Terry and Eric.

"Why don't whi run wha own river boat shuffle," demanded Alex, "ah know who ti get in touch with to hire the boat."

"And ah could get some tickets printed," added Terry.

"The band would do it," said Eric, "if wih could get a piano."

As the pints went down, so the plan evolved and by the end of the night they were all committed to, and excited by, the prospect.

The outcome was that one Saturday morning in April, a strange anarchic group of girls and boys were standing round a piano on the Newcastle quayside waiting for a boat.

Thanks to the increasing prevalence of juke boxes, there was no shortage of pianos standing unused in various pubs around the town. Landlords were glad to be rid of them, so much so that piano-smashing competitions - where the first team to get a piano through a car tyre - were the latest craze. The problem was finding a pub with a superfluous instrument, close enough to the quayside not to require the use of transport.

Fate played one of its more favourable tricks and they located a battered old upright in the Crown Posada, situated half-way down Dean Street; it was downhill all the way to the river. They gathered in the pub for the lunch time session and Pricey tried out the piano. It was out of tune but he made no attempt at tuning it as it would be a lot worse by the time they got it aboard the boat. Three thirty found them roaring down Dean Street with the piano in their midst, not so much pushing, more preventing it from taking off down the bank. Their vessel was due to arrive at 5p.m., so Pricey seated himself on a capstan and ran through a few numbers. A good deal of the profits on these trips was taken over the bar and as Terry took a casual inventory of what was going aboard, it occurred to him that profits might be low on this trip.

Divided among the forty or so prospective passengers there were at least eight demijohns of cider, two bottles of methylated spirit and a bottle of industrial alcohol, not to mention a great many quarter bottles of spirit secreted in various girl's handbags. There was the usual supply of purple hearts, and a certain amount of marijuana, but there was one drug yet to be experienced by any of them. Most of them had read in "On The Road" of a character named Old Bull Lee, alias William Burroughs, who got his kicks from breaking open inhalers and chewing the benzedrene-soaked pad inside. Inspired by this piece of information, Hank had tracked down someone who could supply him with the stuff and lurking in the inside of his leather jacket was a bottle containing enough benzedrene to fill several dozen inhalers.

The boat was now heading for the shore and the captain - all gold braid and whiskers - didn't know what he was in for. Transporting a piano up a gang plank is no easy task, but they managed it without losing anyone overboard and once in place Pricey set about the task of getting it in tune. Johnny set up his drums and Eric checked out his small amp and single mike, then they headed for the bar, where the rest of the band were already well into the beer. Someone once said that musicians are the only people who get drunk before they go to work, so it was obviously going to be some time before there was any music.

Once away from the shore, the magic of the dirty old river took over their senses, the throbbing engine and the rippling water had a calming effect. Pricey sat down at his piano stool, consisting of a couple of beer crates topped off with his white mac and eased his way into "Blue Monk". Gradually the rest of the band joined in and the mellow sound completed the contentment everyone was feeling. However, there was every reason to suppose that matters could be improved even further with the use of a few drugs and Hank, being the purveyor of something new, found himself reaching into his inside pocket at regular intervals. Eric picked up the mike and launched into "Good Morning Little School Girl" one of the many Joe Turner songs in the band's repertoire. From then on it was rhythm and blues all the way and the decks reverberated to dancing feet.

There was precious little traffic on the once bustling Tyne and the little ferry boat chugged down the mainstream without hindrance.

The captain, with no demands being made on his maritime skills, turned his attention to the passengers. He took in the sight of big Alex and company, drinking directly from gallon jars of cider, with thumbs hooked in the handles, forearms supporting the heavy demijohns like regular hillbillies. Discretion being the better part of valour, he decided to let it go. This was his first mistake. However, had he taken a stand against excessive non-licensed cider drinking, he would have been powerless against the covert drug taking going on all around him. Benzedrene, marijuana and purple hearts were all being consumed, along with alcohol in various forms, as the sturdy little vessel cut its way through the calm waters of the Tyne, heading for the sleepy village of Ryton Willows.

Some indication the type of evening in store, may have been deduced by the fact that when the boat had docked, but before the gangplank had been lowered, a wild-eyed, blonde boy named Davie Phipps, could be seen sliding down the mooring rope clutching a bottle of meths. Inspired by this, the rest of the passengers contrived to disembark by any means other than the conventional one, resulting in a great deal of dampness all round. The captain, along with the barman and the crew, - which consisted of one elderly man in a duffle coat - took out their flasks, opened their sandwiches and with some foreboding, settled down to wait for closing time and the return of their passengers.

The passengers meanwhile, were heading for The Ship, the biggest pub in the village and one with a stage, a piano, and a P. A. system. Out in the sticks, people had not yet lost the art of entertaining themselves.

The band were soon in full flow, with Danny, Jeff and Pat booting out riffs in response to Eric's throaty blues shouting on "Bye Bye Baby Blues". Johnny, having supplemented his kit with the resident bass drum and a huge Ziljan cymbal, was driving the band along in a frenzy of rhythm. The piano - for once - was in good order and Pricey was on form. Making up for the lack of a bass player with his powerful left hand, he made the miked-up instrument jump for joy. All this had the required effect on the audience. People were dancing from the very first song and the music of the cash register filled the landlord's heart with joy as the boys filled up on some decent draught beer. Interval time came too soon and the musicians spilled off the stage for a well-earned rest and a chance to drink some of the pints lined up for them. Danny and Pat slipped out for some fresh air and a toke on their own preferred stimulant.

Now was the time for talk and Terry drifted out of several conversations, finally heading off with Alex and Hank to sample the wares of the other pubs in the village. As they made their way back across the village green, they could already hear the band in full swing again, with the Ray Charles classic "What'd I Say", Johnny making excellent use of the cymbal on the complex drum part and Jeff booting away on tenor in his own interpretation of the great Fathead Newman. They reflected for a while on just how good the band were, before plunging back into the smoke filled room and the full blast of heat and noise.

The second half passed without untoward incident. There was a certain amount of dancing on the tables and even some running along the bar, but as long as nothing was broken, the landlord, - conscious perhaps of the swelling bar takings - did not seem to mind. Closing time came too soon, but they all knew that the night was still young so, without the usual haggling for another pint, they headed for their waterborne transport.

One or two were too far gone on drink and did not make it on board, but that was made up for by three local girls who had been inveigled into making the trip, plus one seriously drunk man, whom they named the drunken sot and who was destined for a lost weekend.

The boat slipped its moorings and slid into midstream. It was a clear night and the river reflected the blackness of the sky, the tiny vessel disturbing the reflection of the stars as it cut through the limpid waters. The engines murmured softly, relying on the power of the seaborne current to move them eastwards. For a while all was calm, apart from Animal and Red standing at the prow of the boat invoking the blessings of the Nordic god Odin.

After a while Pricey began to finger out a slow blues, Jeff picked up his tenor and breathed out an accompaniment, while Johnny filled in with some soft brushwork, Danny and Pat joined in and soon the band was playing again. They had already exhausted their repertoire, so after a couple of extemporaneous numbers they began their set again, their performance seeming little impaired by the amount of drink and drugs they had ingested. They were soon in full flight on the Ray Charles classic, "Drown In My Own Tears"; everyone knew the song and joined in the chorus, swaying back and forth, some dangerously close to the edge. Terry hoped the song would not prove too prophetic, as the audience were bopping round the boat with an abandon bordering on the reckless. The three Ryton girls were plied with drink and drugs and the drunken sot was handed an abandoned demijon of cider, which he accepted with a gracious slobber.

Later on in the voyage, Spud was seen emerging from the tiny toilet, with a filthy leer on his face and his arm round one of the Ryton girls. She arrived just in time to see her friend, showing a great deal of blotchy white thigh, while being violently sick over the side. After his sordid sexual triumph, Spud decided it would be excellent sport to circumnavigate the boat on the outside, clinging to whatever was available. His example was soon followed by several other lunatics; eventually at least a quarter of the passengers were somewhere other than the deck. And the band played on.

The frantic captain shouted himself hoarse trying to take command of the situation, but eventually he gave up and simply opened up the throttle, increasing the rate of knots to the maximum the little ferry would stand. The throbbing engines seemed to synchronise with the music for a while and then the speed increased as they entered the part of the river influenced by the tide, which was obviously on the wane and sucking them towards the sea. At this point Spud and Davey Phipps spotted the lights of their home village of Chopwell on the starboard bow. They decided that this was their stop and without hesitation they dived into the murky waters and swam for the shore. Terry panicked and began shouting, "man overboard" and breaking out the lifebelts before Hank took him in hand.

"Divn't worry Terry man, they both learned to swim in the river when thi wha just little kids. Spud reckons it's not so bad as long as yih divn't mind the turds bumping off yah lips".

With that he headed for the bar, for one more drink before they reached the quayside.

As they passed under the Redheugh bridge, the captain throttled back, not wishing to overshoot his destination and the unloading of his - by now - unwanted passengers.

The band had also headed for the bar and Terry joined them. The subject under discussion was how they would return the piano to the shore. Alex and Red came up with a solution.

"It must be sacrificed to the Tyne gods", "roared Red.

"Yes," bellowed Alex, "the gods of the river must have music."

Within minutes an enthusiastic team of drunken furniture removers was formed and the old upright was balanced on the stern of the boat. The captain, detecting a change in the equilibrium of the vessel, turned, just in time to see the piano disappear overboard, to the accompaniment of discordant cheers, cries of Odin, the shouting of a great many nautical terms and the dancing of what everyone fondly imagined was a hornpipe. Johnny played a succession of drum rolls while Jeff played "What Shall We Do With The Drunken Sailor" on his tenor.

The bewhiskered seafarer was apoplectic with rage; he bounded down his ladder swearing mightily and with fists flying. The crowd parted and using his own momentum, they helped him overboard to join the piano, which was already sinking. The crew of one grabbed a life belt and threw it in the general direction of the captain who was managing to swim and curse at the same time.

With no one at the helm the boat was drifting with the current and looked likely to pull away from the shore. Hank grabbed the wheel and inexpertly guided it to the quayside where it ground its way to a halt against the coping stones. There was enough of the boat touching the quay for them to disembark and this they did with alacrity. Everyone pitched in to carry the band's gear and they raced away from the quayside towards Dean Street, leaving the three female stowaways tottering around the deck in their high heels unable to make the leap. The drunken sot was sleeping peacefully on the grubby deck, next to a neat pile of vomit, on which his false teeth balanced precariously.

In an effort to get out of sight quickly, they turned left and panted along The Close, then up the Castle Stairs that wound their way up the steep river bank to the Bridge Hotel and the Black Gate Museum situated at the entrance to the High Level Bridge. At the first landing they stopped to recover their breath, then set off again and made it to the top where they lay down on the old cobble stones and giggled helplessly.

People began to drift away, but the main body slipped along the quiet back lane known as Forth Banks which ran behind the Central Station and led to the Railway Canteen. Once they were there, among the other night people, they felt safe and were soon troughing down pie and chips, drinking mugs of tea and re-living the night's events in the first incarnation of a tale that would be told many times.

Terry walked home with Danny and Pat, up Westmorland Road to East Parade. The sparrows were just beginning their early morning discordant chorus when he finally fell into bed to sleep the morning away, then wake with a troubled conscience, or at least some foreboding of trouble ahead.

In the next few days everyone expected a threatening letter, a visit from the police, or a gang of hairy-arsed seamen visiting the Old George intent on revenge, but nothing happened, there were no repercussions. The Tyne Gods must have liked their piano!

Rumble in Alnwick

Things were not going well for Danny and Pat - work on the building sites was sporadic and poorly paid. They were not getting enough gigs as musicians to supplement their income; what they got from playing with the Kansas City Seven barely paid their beer money. Occasionally they would travel back to visit their old haunts around Moss Side in Manchester to look up old friends and score some dope.

On one of these visits they were approached by bandleader Eric Deans whose all-black orchestra was doing well in that area. He needed an alto player and a trumpeter, would they like a job? This was an offer that was hard to turn down. There was more work in Manchester and more life, so after some soul searching they decided to make the move. Of course the crowd were sad to see them go, especially the band, but everyone realised it was a good career move. A farewell party was held at which Danny and Pat became very emotional about their Newcastle friends and promised to keep in touch, which they did.

Sadly, Pat was to die in the early nineties but Danny was to remain a regular correspondent and visitor to the North East. He recently confessed that when he first met Eric and his mates he was very wary of white people, having had some bad experiences with racism, including being beaten up. He claims that it was only his time spent with the crowd that changed his life and made him realise that all white people are not bad. A heartening thought, but at the same time a damning indictment of the treatment of black people in Britain at that time.

Once Danny and Pat departed from East Parade, the landlord asked Terry to move into their room as the health inspectors had condemned the basement as unfit for human habitation. He was sorry to make the move but at least he had a view of the overgrown gardens opposite and could observe the sordid pageant of life on the street.

He had long ago given up trying to manage the band but he did suggest that they consider recruiting George Stoves to play electric guitar as he had heard him play blues and was sure he would fit in. They held the audition in the Downbeat on a Saturday afternoon, club manager Mike Jeffries being amenable to the idea. In fact, he was happy for them to use the place for practice every Saturday

**The Kansas City 5
at the Downbeat**

afternoon. The band now became the Kansas City Five with Eric, Pricey and Johnny plus Jeff Hedley on tenor with George on electric guitar, still no bass player.

Once George had been assimilated into the band they made a much tighter sound which seemed to impress Mike Jeffries to the extent that he offered them a Friday night spot at the club, their first regular paid work. They soon built up a following with people other than the Simpsons crowd and The Squatters.

The climate was changing, people were looking for something new. This ragged crew who did not wear band uniforms and smoked and drank on stage began to attract the new generation of disaffected youth, or at least the ones who discovered The Downbeat. The casual style affected by the crowd was now becoming the norm, jeans and combat jackets proliferated, suits and ties were out.

Without Danny and Pat, Terry began to feel rather vulnerable living in East Parade. Two of the Doyles' male children had turned into teenagers overnight and eyed him like young tigers stalking their prey whenever he walked by. Twice his room was broken into when he was away for the weekend and his gas meter smashed open for the few shillings it contained, although his records, record player and personal belongings were left untouched. The Rickets brothers obviously bore a grudge, favouring him with ugly looks whenever he was unfortunate enough to pass them on the stairs.

Meanwhile the landlord, having given the basement walls a good coating of bitumen and some cheap wallpaper, rented out the rooms again. Terry's old room housed a black bus conductor and his white girl friend who also worked on the buses. They were a sweet couple, very much in love, a love that was sorely tried by the racist taunts they had to endure. The old practice room, with the piano still intact, was also rented out to a mixed-race couple who Terry imagined did not suffer too much criticism over their alliance.

Stevie was a huge man, black as ebony, and well over six feet tall, who wore a long black overcoat and a black fedora. When he smiled his easy smile, gold glinted among the white tombstone teeth. He reminded Terry of the legendary Stackerlee who featured in so many blues songs and carried a six gun in his pocket and a razor in his shoe. Whether Stevie carried any weapons, or what his line of business was, he did not care to ask, but for some reason he did not feel afraid of, or threatened by him and the big man for his part always spoke to Terry with courtesy. His partner was a tall, heavily made-up girl, with a great deal of black hair piled up on the top of her head, and a penchant for very high heels and fur coats. The relationship was a very uneasy one. Terry would often come home late and find her sitting on the stairs with her mascara smudged by tears, obviously locked out for the night. There was little he could do other than sneak her out a cup of coffee and a biscuit. The next afternoon, on returning home from work, he would find the spotlessly clean cup outside his door.

The band gave up on the Wednesday night spot at the New Orleans Club, but the crowd continued to attend the club on Saturday nights before going on to the all night session at the Downbeat. Couples began to predominate. Bill and Margaret were always together, along with Stan and Paula, Joe and Anne, Eric and Doreen, and of course Terry and Helen.

One night Johnny arrived with a new girl friend, a willowy blonde by the name of Julie. He and she worked on the third storey in offices on opposite sides of the street, and had taken to waving to each other. Eventually Johnny asked her out by printing his request on a sheet of wallpaper and holding it up at the window. Even Pricey had taken enough time away from the piano to find himself a girl. She was a small curvaceous brunette called Sheila who clung to Pricey at all times and had little to say to the rest of the crowd.

Johnny and Pricey continued to play mid-week gigs at the Marimba and with the addition of string bass player Alan Black they turned into a tasteful jazz trio eminently suitable for their cellar club surroundings.

Not satisfied with the Downbeat and the Marimba, budding

Johnny & Julie at the New Orleans

impresario Mike Jeffries was now planning a third enterprise. Having located suitable premises above the Handysides Arcade on Percy Street, he was in the process of converting it into a more up market night club. Always one for using his contacts, he enlisted Eric to design and decorate the interior. As with little Joe's efforts at the Downbeat, his imagination was allowed full rein. This was a long term prospect and Eric was not about to rush things, so he still managed to have his fair share of long pub lunchtimes and weekends away with the Squatters.

One such weekend they were off to Alnwick and were keen on Pricey and Eric to join them as there were plenty of pubs with pianos. Jean Reay, Paula and some of the other girls were going, so Terry persuaded Helen to break out her rucksack and come along. The two of them set off together on Saturday morning walking out of town on the Great North Road, past the Hancock Museum and the Exhibition Park, until they were a reasonable distance out of town on the stretch of road that flanked the Town Moor.

It was a bright morning, which usually boded well for lifts, so they placed their rucksacks at their feet, stuck out their thumbs and tried to look appealing. Two hours later they were sitting in the Dusty Bottles in Alnwick, a tiny pub on the way down to the river where they had arranged to meet the rest. This ancient hostelry appealed to the squatters as it had a window display that had not been disturbed for over two hundred years. According to local legend the person decorating the window had dropped down dead and anyone touching the display would suffer the same fate.

Gradually the motley crew filtered in, filling the bar with people, rucksacks and bindles. Pricey and Eric turned up but as the place had no piano their services were not called upon. On hearing of the legend, Noddy and Spud proved not to be superstitious and had to be restrained from climbing into the window to see if there was anything left in the dusty old bottles.

The landlord had the usual problems turfing them out at closing time, but three-thirty found them crossing the bridge over the lovely River Aln and heading out of town. Big Alex led the way up hill across a couple of fields to an old Dutch barn containing a few bales of straw, sufficient to provide a hiding place for the gear and provide shelter in the evening. Gear stashed, they set off back down hill. After climbing a tall fence and walking through a shady copse, they arrived on the banks of the river. Hank built a fire, even though there was nothing to cook - it seemed to stamp their identity on the place.

They spent the afternoon skimming stones, climbing trees and throwing sticks for Willy the dog, who spent a great deal of his time in the river. The girls also ended up in the river, but not by choice. Having suffered this fate more than once, they had come prepared and once the fun was over, they repaired to the barn to change their clothes. Terry refrained from condemning Helen to the same fate, sensing correctly that she would not have been amused.

Pub time soon rolled round and they set off for the town with Hank in the lead and Willy trotting obediently by his side. Terry and Helen found themselves walking behind Alex and Jean. The pair strolled along arm in arm, deep in conversation, interspersed by laughter, totally engrossed in each other, like two people in love. Instinctively Terry reached out for Helen's hand and she smiled in understanding, knowing as he did that they were seeing something blossom and wondering perhaps, whether the same thing could happen to them.

After sampling a few pubs they ended up in the Blue Bell which had more room and a decent piano. Eric had recently discovered a talent for improvising twelve bar blues, where the first line is sung twice and the third line has to rhyme with the first, as in :

"He's mean and he's hairy, he's the guy I dig the most.

He's mean and he's hairy, he's the guy I dig the most.

It's big Alex Baird, he's the scourge of the North East coast."

On this occasion he was working his way around each member of the crowd, attempting to make up a verse about every one. This could be rather boring for an outsider, but not for those involved, who applauded even his more trite efforts.

Pricey was playing a few fills while Eric scanned the audience looking for his next victim, his eyes falling on a group of local Teddy boys standing at the back. Inspiration clouded his judgement and he trotted out a quick verse.

"Well I'm a greasy Ted, I wear a long black drape.

Well I'm a greasy Ted, I wear a long black drape.

My main pre-occupations are drinking, fighting and rape."

Perhaps the Ted did not know what pre-occupations meant, maybe he thought it didn't scan well, or he may have been a sensitive soul. More than likely he just felt like beating someone up.

At any rate, he set off towards Eric with a mouth full of oaths and his fists clenched. Red who was sitting near the front had smuggled in his trusty staff which lay on the floor beside him. Something broke the potential assailant's stride and he sprawled full length on the floor then quickly leapt to his feet, his wrath now directed at Red. The ginger-haired one having replaced the staff was now on his feet, as was Alex, Noddy and several of the others.

The black-draped youth froze, he looked towards his mates, they didn't move. Discretion is the better part of valour and he rejoined his ashamed-looking friends, his face black with fury.

Pricey broke into the opening bars of "Summertime", a cue for Paula to get up and sing and the incident was soon forgotten. The evening ended in its usual barn-storming manner, with much dancing, beer-drinking competitions and the banging of tin trays on heads and various other parts of the body.

Once the landlord had emptied them back onto the pavement, they headed for the chippy just off the village square. Alex proposed that for the sake of the girls, they would eat inside in what was not so much a restaurant, more a canteen, but at least you got to eat with knives and forks.

The meal was almost at an end when a fresh-faced boy of about seventeen entered the establishment. He walked towards Alex and pulled up a chair swinging it round so that he could sit legs akimbo with his forearms leaning on the back, here was a kid who had watched too many movies. He addressed Alex in this manner :- "Yee lot have fuckin had it."

"Oh, really?" said Alex, wolfing down a large piece of haddock, "and why's that?"

"Look oot the winda" came the reply.

They all looked out of the window. It was a long window and ranged along its full length were a selection of youths of various shapes, sizes and ages, who had one thing in common; they all carried a weapon. There were sticks, bicycle chains, pick axe handles and various other lethal-looking objects.

Alex picked up an extra large chip and slowly ground it into the youth's forehead. "Well, yi can tell yah mates ti let the lasses through and when wi've finished wha chips wi'll come and sort yi's out."

The boy returned to his mates wearing a rather fixed grin and wiping his forehead with a grubby handkerchief. "How you gonna get out of this one, Alex?" demanded Jean, "ahm stopping here".

Alex grinned his mischievous grin. "Just get yahselves off," he said, his eyes gleaming devilishly, "ahve got a plan."

After some further protests the girls finally left and the gang outside let them pass with little more than a few obscene remarks, which were more than matched by instant repartee from the girls.

As he watched them go, Terry could not help but wonder what kind of plan could rescue the situation, but no one seemed too concerned. After drinking his tea, Alex got to his feet. "Right, lads.

A few of the Squatters making free with somone elses car

Follow me".

They stepped out in single file, Terry, Eric, and Pricey managed to get themselves in the middle while Hank and Willy brought up the rear. Alex addressed the gang. "Right. Wah ganna get out of the square cos tha's coppers aboot."

He set off across the cobbles at a fair pace with the rest of the squatters bunched round him.

The Alnwick lads followed behind, trying to keep their weapons out of public view. Once across the square. the Squatters rounded a corner and just for a moment were out of sight of their pursuers. That's when Alex put his plan into action. "Run like buggery" he roared, and suiting the words to the deed, he set off at a gallop.

The rest needed no prompting and within seconds they were all pelting down the cobbled street that would eventually lead to the river. Fear and excitement pumped adrenaline through their bodies and in this heightened state of awareness what happened next seemed almost magical.

Huge drops of rain began to spatter the road, within seconds this became a downpour, thunder rent the air and the rain became torrential, quickly soaking them to the skin. Lightning lit up the night revealing the Alnwick lads not far behind, but they were slowing down and their numbers seemed depleted.

Mindful of the fact that they planned to go to the late night dance, some of them had given up the chase and had taken whatever shelter they could find, in a vain attempt to save their suits from a drenching.

By now, water was running in torrents down the cobbled street and the gully down the centre, fulfilling its original function as an open drain, was foaming with water. The drama of the situation was too much for the wild nature of the Squatters they danced in the rushing stream, screaming oaths to the Norse god Odin interspersed with Indian war whoops.

Suddenly aware of the approaching enemy, Animal gave a roar and set off up the hill towards them, followed by the rest of the crowd.

Willy the dog, not the least bit cowed by the storm, took the lead, barking furiously and presenting a fearsome figure with his slavering canines and mane of red hair.

To say that the Squatters had the psychological advantage was a considerable understatement; somehow pickaxe handles and chains seemed of little use against this primeval force. The Alnwick lads fled, their crepe-soled shoes squelching over the gleaming wet cobbles.

Spud and Geronimo picked up a couple of pick-axe handles, then they all turned and carried on down the hill towards the river. By the time they reached the bridge the rain had ceased. The night air smelled sweet after the storm and Terry breathed it in with relish, taking in the scent of the hedgerows and the damp grass, feeling totally and wonderfully alive.

As they headed off across the fields the smell of wood smoke began to predominate. The girls had utilised their fire lighting skills and their shadowy figures could be seen silhouetted against the flames. The boys were soon standing round the blaze steaming gently, while they told the tale of the night's events.

Terry located Helen among the bales at the rear of the Dutch barn. She'd changed her clothes and was combing her long hair. She ran to him. "What happened? I was worried about you."

He took her in his arms and laughed, "if you want to hear the Cecil B. de Mille version wi better get by the fire, the lads are just starting on the epic now."

Some time later, when the fire had died down, a dark figure came stumbling across the field towards them. Instinctively they drew back from the light, but they need not have worried. What appeared out of the darkness was not an enemy, or a stranger. It was Noddy.

"Where the hell have yi been, man?" demanded Red.

"Ahv been ti the fuckin dance, man. Where wa ye?"

Without waiting for an answer, he carried on.

"Them fuckin locals have been using me as a football, man. Mind you," he chuckled, "ah fettled aboot six i them before ah went doon. Hey man ahm covered in lumps, it's just as well thi wa wearin crepe soles. Hey man, ahv never been si glad ti see the fuckin coppers in me life."

So he went on in this vein and although he was indeed, "covered in lumps" it did not prevent him from breaking out into a hearty chuckle at regular intervals as his story unfolded.

Long before the others had finished talking and singing the night away, Terry and Helen had faded back among the bales and climbed into his double sleeping bag. There was only one way to express the elation he felt.

The next morning, they all headed off down to the river to wash themselves, cook breakfast and dry out their clothes in the morning sun. Hank cooked up a pan of lites for Willy and they amused themselves feeding the ravenous dog.

Geronimo went off into the woods for a shit and came back with three shits, all wearing tweeds and carrying shotguns. They had the look of gamekeepers and although the guns were broken open and pointed at the ground in safety mode, Terry could see the glint of cartridges in the breech. The one with the best clothes and most expensive-looking gun stepped forward and spoke with the quiet authority of one born to power.

"Exactly what do you think you are doing?"

"Having wha breakfast" said Spud with a cheeky grin.

"Don't you realise this is private land?" demanded one of the other men in a threatening manner.

The first man carried on in the same measured tones. "Yes, he is correct, it is and I would like you off it as soon as you have finished your breakfast," with a nod in Spud's direction.

He turned to go. "And I hope that you'll tidy up before you leave". "Who are you anyway?" asked Hank.

"I am the Duke of Northumberland. Good morning gentlemen, and ladies."

With that, he strode off into the woods with his two lackeys by his side. "You know", said Alex "ahm beginning to think wha not welcome in this town, it's Starward Gorge for me next week were wi can get a bit of peace and quiet".

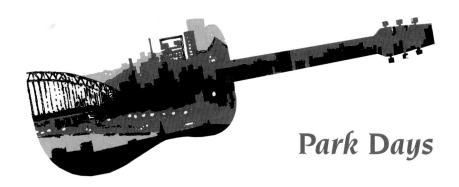

Park Days

Now that the summer weather had really established itself, Terry and George resumed their lunchtime visits to the park and, though he never mentioned, it Terry always hoped to bump into Hazel. Whenever he saw a young girl pushing a pram his heart would skip a beat and he would make some pretence to get near her, only to be disappointed. George knew exactly what was going on and it was he who finally spotted her. "There's that tart yi fancy" he said indicating a figure near the swings.

"What tart," he asked as he looked across and recognised her? "Yi mean Hazel, ah don't fancy ah man, wha just friends."

"Aye and ah divvent fancy Marilyn Monroe. Look ahll just leave you to it, ahm not in the mood for playing gooseberry."

Terry made no protest, he was already on his way towards the swings.

Hazel was wearing blue jeans and he realised that he had never seen her in anything but skirts and dresses. Little Charlotte was dressed in a pale green dress and a straw bonnet with matching ribbon. She sat in her pushchair awaiting her turn on the baby swings while her mother rocked her gently back and forth.

He stood observing them for a while, until Hazel turned and saw him. She did not seem surprised and putting the brake on the pushchair, stretched out her arms and offered her mouth to be kissed. "I knew I would see you today," she said,

"I just had a feeling".

She stepped back to the child and knelt down beside her.

"Charlotte, here's yah uncle Terry to see you". Terry went down on his haunches and took the little girl's hand. "Pleased to meet you".

Her hair was as red as her mother's and as prophesied her eyes were vivid green. She smiled a greeting. "Daddy," she said.

Terry was taken aback. "Don't worry", laughed Hazel, "she hasn't got any inside information, she calls all men Daddy at the moment".

A swing soon became vacant and Terry pushed the little girl while she squealed with delight, her cheeks flushed with excitement. When she tired of this sport, the three of them went to the lake where Terry amused the child by feeding the ducks, sacrificing a good proportion of his sandwiches. Too soon, it was time for him to go. "Will you be here next week?", he asked casually. "I can be" she smiled. "Only ahll tell George, it'll save him", his voice trailed off. "Having his sandwiches on his own" she supplied. "Aye, he can always stay in the canteen and play cards, so ahll see you next Wednesday, weather permitting". So they saw each other every Wednesday through that summer and if the weather did not permit, they went to the museum of Science and Technology keeping Charlotte amused by trying the many hands-on exhibits. But mostly the weather was fine so they went boating, swinging, or just lay on the grass playing with the little girl and enjoying each other's company. An ice cream vendor sold his wares from a hand-pushed cart containing a huge metal churn of vanilla ice-cream. This was Gazillee's ice cream, the best in Newcastle in Terry's opinion, containing so much vanilla that it was dark cream in colour. His favourite was a sugar cornet with a squirt of monkey's blood (raspberry syrup) on top. He would buy the ice creams and they would tie on Charlotte's bib and watch while she covered herself from head to foot in the delicious confection.

As the weeks passed, Terry was fascinated to watch her progress and considered himself fortunate to be there when she took her first steps. Her vocabulary improved day by day and to his delight she was soon able to say his name.

"What's yah husband gonna say when she starts talking about this bloke called Terry?", he asked Hazel one day.

She wrinkled her nose in annoyance. "He never sees ah, she's always in bed by the time he gets home and weekends he's off playing golf or boozing with his friends. Anyway, I'm entitled to have a friend, so if he doesn't like it he can lump it."

Just for a moment, tears welled up in her eyes but she wiped them away and smiled. "Sorry, I didn't mean to sound all silly and twisted" she said - paraphrasing a catch-line from the Goon Show. "I know he works hard to provide for us, it's just sometimes I feel so alone."

"So that's why you need me" said Terry.

"No, Terry, I'd want to see you no matter what my situation was, but mebee we shouldn't see each other quite so often."

So as Autumn crept up on them they saw each other less and less, but she would still ring him at work occasionally and arrange to meet in Fenwicks' cafeteria and Charlotte still remembered his name.

Work on Mike Jeffries' new club was progressing slowly because of lack of money, although it now had a name: it was to be called the Club A-Go-Go. One Wednesday night Terry was in Simpsons with Eric, Johnny and a few of the rest of the crowd when little Joe Pharoe arrived to tell them that the Marimba had burned down the night before. Johnny was on his feet in an instant - his drums were in the cellar, along with Alan Black's double bass. Everyone drank up and rushed off to see the damage.

The building was a smoke-blackened wreck, but the stairs to the cellar were intact. They made their way downstairs, where there was enough light from the pavement level windows to see that the bass and drums were alright, despite standing in four inches of water. "Ah hope he's insured", said Terry.

"Divn't worry", laughed Eric, "he's insured alright and now he's got some money to finish the A-Go-Go."

"Yeah, very convenient," agreed Johnny,. "Well, ah wish he had told me so ah could of got me drums out."

So that was one less gig for Johnny and Pricey and more work for Eric. They all hoped that the new club would be open soon.

Nothing exciting was happening on the pop front and they approached Christmas with balladeers like Shirley Bassey, Adam Faith and Billy Fury dominating the British charts.

In America, Tamla Motown had their first hit with "Please Mr Postman" by The Marvelettes. They in their turn were raving about an eleven year old singer/harmonica player called Steveland Judkins who they nicknamed Little Stevie Wonder.

The comparative affluence of the late Fifties brought about a great many changes and increased expectations among working-class people. Arguably the most profound change was the increase in home ownership among a stratum of society previously happy to live in decent council housing. Among Terry's crowd, buying a house was never a topic up for discussion until Bill Davidson announced that he and Margaret were about to be married and, furthermore, they intended to buy a house. Given Bill's job at a building society and the added perk of a cheap mortgage, it seemed the obvious thing to do.

Up until that time private landlords owned huge tracts of terraced houses, but uncertainty about rent controls and the availability of cheap mortgages tempted them to sell for a quick profit. Bill and

Margaret bought a terraced house in West Jesmond, situated near the railway station, also conveniently close to a large pub called The Lonsdale.

This seemed to Terry the perfect answer to his fraught situation at East Parade. To buy a house one needed a deposit of at least two hundred and fifty pounds. He had recently completed his apprenticeship and was earning a basic wage of twelve pounds a week, plus overtime. He stepped up his payments to his building society savings account, another fifty pounds was all he needed. Meanwhile East Parade would have to do, and his friends still found it a useful place to go midweek when money was tight.

One Wednesday night, Terry and Helen emerged from the Pavilion picture house in the company of Eric and Doreen. The movie was "Gun Fever", an off-beat western, filmed in black and white with un-scripted dialogue and unknown actors. Shot on location in a dirty shanty town, with an equally filthy cast of badly dressed ruffians, it looked authentic. This was how they had always imagined the real West to be, a far cry from the Westerns currently being churned out by the likes of Randolph Scott and Audie Murphy.

The pavements were wet from recent rain when they emerged and the evening mist was fast turning the polluted air into a city smog. Smokeless zones were as yet unheard of and the fumes from thousands of chimneys blackened the buildings and begrimed the streets. They had attended the first house so the night was young, but funds were low. Terry suggested coffee back at his place and despite the inclement weather they decided to walk. They set off up Westgate Road four abreast through the swirling mist, their way illuminated by gas lamps whose light softened by a halo of cotton wool highlighted their excited young faces as they floated in and out of the shadows. The pavements were deserted and there were few cars on the road. An occasional bus ground its way up the hill in low gear, its occupants almost totally obscured by the filth thrown up from the wet dirty streets. They chatted and walked ,enjoying the unusual conditions, the dark shadows seeming an extension of the dark shadowy film they had so recently watched.

Eventually they reached the big lamp at the top of Westgate Road and forked left for Elswick. As they walked down East Parade they passed the tiny convent and the crucifix, with the life-sized statue of Jesus Christ impaled upon it, appeared out of the mist. "Yi'd think them nuns would have given im an overcoat in this weather", quipped Eric. "Aye, he'll catch he's death in this weather " said Terry, "whatever happened to Christian charity?". Jesus continued to stare into the middle distance wearing a beatific expression, no doubt he had heard worse comments on this street.

Once inside, Terry soon had the fire blazing and the coffee made while Eric put on a Gerry Mulligan record. Somehow, light seemed an intrusion so he lit a couple of candles. Eric and Doreen sat together on the bed while Helen and Terry sprawled on the settee in front of the fire. After a while, conversation began to fade, the two on the bed, totally engrossed in each other, and probably expecting Terry and Helen to be the same, but it was not so.

Eventually, Helen decided she must catch her bus home and Terry reached gratefully for his coat. They walked up the street in silence, and after a while they realised that they had company. A small wire haired mongrel, a cross-breed of several types of terrier, was trotting behind them. They stopped and bent down to stroke him but he backed away, observing them with bright inquisitive eyes. As they set off again he trotted along behind, eventually walking by their side as if he were their very own pet. The smog was now so thick that Jesus was almost invisible and appeared to be floating in mid-air like some ghostly apparition. They ploughed on hand in hand but still strangely silent. Luckily the bus stop was situated next to a gas lamp, so they stood in a murky pool of light listening for the bus and the little dog sat on its hind legs waiting with them. Terry brushed Helen's long hair back from her shoulders and addressed her gruffly. "Tha mad about each other those two, in love," he ventured.

She smiled a wistful smile. "Very much so, it made you feel uncomfortable."

" Or jealous," said Terry.

Then he knew what he had to say. "Look, Helen, don't you think we're just wasting each other's time, we keep seeing each other, but wha never gonna have what they've got, ah mean ah like you a lot, you're a great person, but there's just something missing."

She turned away and gazed into the mist. "I knew this was coming, it was just a matter of time."

Just then the terrier gave a short throaty bark. She looked down and grinned ruefully. "Ruff, ahll say it's rough."

She bent down to stroke the dog and this time it allowed her to pet it. She stood up and faced him, thrusting her hands deep into the pockets of her duffle coat. She looked so beautiful and vulnerable that he felt like changing his mind.

"Okay Terry, I think you're probably right. Perhaps I just didn't want to admit it, but I'll miss you and I'll miss the crowd."

"You don't have to leave the crowd", he said. "We can still be friends."

The dog gave a long low howl. "Right on cue", she laughed. "Are you sure you haven't got this animal trained, Molloy"?

Glad of the release in tension, he laughed and held her tight, and at that moment the bus came lumbering out of the darkness. They waved madly and it ground to a halt. He kissed her hard before she stepped onto the platform and then she was gone, swallowed up by the mist.

"That's it then, laddie" he said addressing the dog, "Ah only hope ahve done the right fuckin' thing."

With that he turned up his collar and headed for home with Laddie trotting beside him.

Reflecting that Eric and Doreen probably would not welcome any company at this juncture, he walked past East Parade and turned down the next street, West Parade, towards the Dodds Arms. On the way he passed a chip shop, and he looked down at the dog, "Poor little bastard's probably starving", he thought, "and ahm a bit peckish meself."

He searched in his pocket and counted out five shillings and sixpence, more than enough to buy fish and chips and still have enough left for a pint.

Laddie looked up expectantly, his tail wagging furiously, when Terry stepped out of the shop with the steam rising from the open package. He tore the fish in half and threw one piece to the excited animal, who wolfed it down in seconds. Taking a bite from his half, he consigned the rest to the hungry creature and concentrated on eating his chips. With supper over, it was time for a drink and he left the little dog at the door as he entered the seedy environs of the pub.

The place was unusually quiet - nothing could be heard but the click of dominoes and the thwack of darts. He was happy to prop up the bar, gaze at his reflection in the mirror and think about what he had done. Two pints later it was closing time and in a mood of intense melancholy he stepped outside expecting to find Laddie but the little dog was gone.

Back at number nine he opened the door very slowly. As expected Eric and Doreen were in bed, but by now lost in post-coital slumber, they did not stir when he closed the door. He did not switch on the light, there was sufficient illumination from the flickering fire light. The pair had fallen asleep in each other's arms, the velvet blackness of Doreen's skin in sharp contrast to Eric's city pallor. He did not wake them - Doreen would have missed her last bus by now. Winding up his alarm clock, he pulled his sleeping bag from the cupboard, settled down on the settee and fell asleep thinking of Helen.

Rhythm
& Blues

Terry determined to live a life free of complications from now on, young free and single - that was the way to be. The band was attracting a young crowd including a fair sprinkling of young ladies, providing him with dancing partners if nothing else.

If one was craving carnal delights the Saturday all night sessions at the Downbeat proved more fruitful. The club's easy going policy meant that many people arrived with sleeping bags and slept on the dance floor when the gig ended in the early hours. Occasionally a girl out for the night and with an adventurous spirit could be persuaded that a double bed and the promise of a cooked breakfast would be preferable to a hard dance floor.

As time went by and the club became better known, the liberal policy came to be abused by the inevitable drunken trouble-makers. Not wishing to have the police prying into his business and unable to deal with it himself, Mike Jeffries turned to employing bouncers. These gentlemen, of course, are just bigger, tougher versions of the people they are employed to control, as many club owners have found to their cost. The bouncers inevitably have equally muscular friends who never pay to get in and seldom pay for drinks. Eventually the luckless owner finds himself no longer in charge of his own club. This situation soon began to prevail at the Downbeat and the crowd watched with amusement as Jeffries used all his powers of diplomacy to keep matters under control.

Friday was Terry's favourite night of the week. He would meet the band and the rest of the crowd in the Grape Vaults to drink wonderful nectarous Exhibition ale. They would sit in the back room commandeering a couple of the long brass and copper tables and order up tray after tray of halves of the pale strong beer, served by an ever-attendant waiter, then off to the Downbeat where only bottled beer was on offer. It was not unusual for the band to be late on stage because of the excellence of the Ex. More blues recordings were becoming available in Britain and this was influencing the band's choice of material. Their own interpretations of T - Bone Walker's "Stormy Monday", Rolling Stone recorded by Muddy Waters and John Lee Hooker's "Boom Boom", sounded exciting and new to their young fans. They thought they were doing something unique but at the same time in London, Alexis Korner and Cyril Davies founded Blues Incorporated, playing music inspired by black American blues artistes, albeit in a different style. This band was to include Mick Jagger, Brian Jones, Charlie Watts, Keith Richards, Ginger Baker and Jack Bruce in its ever-changing line ups. Rhythm & Blues was fast becoming the in thing on the London scene, with musicians such as John Mayall, Long John Baldry, Eric Clapton and Jimmy Page, drifting in and out of various bands. They were vying with and playing at the same venues as established trad bands and, as money was involved, competition was sometimes bitter. In Newcastle. the Kansas City Five could have carved out their own niche but it was not to be. One Friday night, May the eighteenth 1962 Johnny was later to note in his diary, things changed. Johnny and Terry were downing a few swift halves in the Grape Vaults. Johnny was running late - he had already set up his drums at the club then nipped out for some decent ale. They stepped out of the side door into the alley that led to Pilgrim Street, then down Worswick Street towards the Downbeat at a smart pace. They need not have worried. Eric and the rest of the band were hanging round the bar - Pricey was also late. Half an hour later he was still missing so they were forced to play the set without him which, as they still had no bass player, made for a pretty flat sound. It did not take long to discover that Pricey had been poached by Chas Chandler of The Kontors. This band may not been doing anything ground-breaking - just covers of chart songs - but they were making money and Pricey desired more than anything to make a living out of playing music. There was no way of replacing Pricey so the Kansas City Five disintegrated, just at a time when fashion was turning their way and other people involved in the Rhythm & Blues movement were destined to achieve recognition beyond the realms of their imagination.

Change was in the air and the group destined to be most influential in bringing about this change had just won a record deal with E.M.I. and were packing out the Cavern Club in their home town of Liverpool. The Beatles' first single "Love Me Do" only made the lower reaches of the charts although it was constantly played on Radio Luxembourg. Terry first heard it on this crackly commercial radio station, taking particular note of the distinctive harmonica introduction.

Terry's break up with Helen coincided with the petering out of Johnny's relationship with Julie, so the two friends were free to roam together, enjoying each other's company, choosing comradeship over romance, but always keeping one eye on the beautiful girls of Newcastle. They went to the cinema together and indulged in their old hobby of pub-crawling round the more sleazy hostelries in town, sticking to the public bars, always the least salubrious area of any drinking establishment. Anyone looking even vaguely affluent would invariably be approached by a dosser or bar-fly with a request for drink money. The supplicant would always have a tale to tell and the two boys would evaluate his story and give points. Anything up to eight points earned a half, but less than three would earn nothing. Very occasionally a ten pointer would qualify for a pint. These jaunts invariably resulted in the two boys becoming as drunk or drunker than the dissolute inhabitants of this other world.

At the Downbeat they continued to hunt for good dancing partners, especially those with slight imperfections, broadening their range to include slightly prominent teeth and unusual moles. One night they encountered two girls who were remarkably free of imperfections, each one being both beautiful and graceful. One was slim with short dark hair and boyish hips and a generous mouth, the other had long blonde hair and was slender to the point of being skinny. Chubby Chequer had recently achieved chart success with "Let's Twist Again" and the dance craze "The Twist" was dominating the country's dance floors but - even though these girls were young - these girls were jiving. In time-honoured fashion the two boys bowled onto the floor and asked if they could split them up. After a few moment's hesitation the two young ladies acquiesced and allowed themselves to be separated. Without hesitation Johnny reached for the dark haired girl and Terry for the blonde and they proceeded to a clear a space among the rest of the dancers who were putting their sacroiliacs out of kilter by doing "The Twist". The four seemed to get on well together and spent the rest of the evening together. The willowy blonde was called Jenni Black and Johnny's lovely partner was Ann Armstrong. Terry never met Jenni again after that night, but Johnny was destined to see a great deal more of Ann.

Johnny Steel

The Club A-Go-Go finally opened and the whole crowd went to the inaugural night which featured the Mike Carr Trio, with Mike on piano, Malcolm Cecil, bass and John McLaughlan, guitar. Mike was the most popular exponent of modern jazz in the North East in the early sixties and a great many talented musicians were showcased in the various line-ups of his groups, The

Emcee Four. The Emcee Five and The Mike Carr Trio. Some of this great music, privately recorded at Morten Sound Studios, re-issued in the Nineties by Birdland Records under the title "The Emcee Five Bebop From The East Coast". Featured on various tracks are Mike's brother Ian (trumpet); Gary Cox (tenor), bass players John O'Carrrol, Spike Heatly and Midge Pike, with drummers Ronnie Stephenson, Johnny Butts and Jackie Denton.

The club seemed shiny and new - compared to the shabby old Downbeat - with a well-sprung dance floor, well-lit stage with a baby grand piano and a properly equipped bar. Eric had painted a huge mural behind the stage featuring Jazz musicians and several large paintings on the same theme hung round the walls. There was a separate room for the younger set, featuring the ubiquitous disco music that was fast taking the place of live bands in so many clubs.

Among the people present on the first night were Bill and Margaret Davidson, out for the first time after a spate of furniture buying and house decorating. Apart from Terry they were the only ones with their own place and when they had a house warming party it became the first of many and their new home became the focal point for the whole crowd. Bill had indulged himself in the purchase of a brand new stereo record, one of the first of its kind, making him the envy of all. Although a lover of Jazz and Blues Bill was also very fond of music and owned recordings by local artistes such as Lou Killen and The Elliots of Birtley, also American singer/songwriters such as Woody Guthrie, Cisco Houston, Huddie Ledbetter - better known as Leadbelly - and Rambling Jack Elliot. The most recent addition to his collection was the first album of a young American in the Guthrie mould named Bob Dylan. Dylan, although singing the same kind of music as Elliot and Guthrie, somehow invested it with a vitality and urgency, which immediately registered with this group of young urban Geordies. No-one realised that his name was pronounced Dillon, so for a few months they were all fans of Bob Die-lan. Whether Dillon or Die-lan, young Bob turned out to be a major influence on them all, particularly the musicians in the crowd.

Parties at Bill and Margaret's place became regular events, usually going on into the early hours of the morning and involving several people staying the night. Margaret did not seem to mind, but it was hardly the best way to start off a marriage. Terry usually found his way home, usually on the all night bus, but more often he would walk across the city in the early hours, enjoying the silence of the empty streets, passing other solitary drunks or the occasional pair of coppers who would eye him suspiciously but never took the trouble to stop him.

One Sunday morning, after such an occasion, his drunken stupor was penetrated by a gentle knocking. Gradually he became aware that the sound was not in his head but the product of some outside agent. He staggered to the door, opened it and peered out cautiously. Hazel was standing there, her green eyes showing uncertainty and distress. She was dressed for the weather with bright red coat, black beret and scarf. A cold wind was blowing through the ever open front door. "Hazel" he said with some relief, "Come on in and close the door" he said while diving for the warmth of the blankets.

"There's a fire made up if you want to light it".

There were matches on the mantle-piece and she bent down to light the bed of paper, sticks and coal, but drew back with a start when a small mouse leapt from the heap dragging with it a large piece of bacon rind. "Don't worry," laughed Terry, "that's Eccles, he lives in the coal cupboard and eats the coal, ah don't mind cos he doesn't seem to have a family."

Hazel came from a mining community and had no difficulty in coaxing the fire into a healthy blaze, giving the room some semblance of warmth.

"So warra you doing here?" he finally got round to asking, "and where's Charlotte?"

"I left her at me mam's," came the reply. "I'm supposed to be at church."

Terry made no reply to this and watched with some interest, as she removed her hat, scarf, coat and shoes, quickly followed by her sweater, skirt and stockings. She stood before him in her red underwear, her flesh goose-pimpled by the chill and her nipples, engorged by the cold sticking through the lace of her bra. Wrenching his eyes from her breasts, he noticed ugly bruising on her shoulder and ribs. She climbed into his bed and into his arms, pressing her cold body against him, soaking up his warmth.

"Make love to me, Terry," she whispered.

Although he was more than eager to respond, he suddenly became aware of his fetid breath and stubbled chin. With regret he clambered out of bed, put on his duffel coat and baseball boots and headed for the bathroom on the landing. He returned clean, but freezing and poked desparately at the fire, before slipping back between the sheets. By now she was naked and their roles were reversed, she was as warm as he was cold. The whole business was becoming farcical. He reached out to cradle her in his arms and she winced as she turned towards him.

"How come you're all bruised, Hazel?" he asked, looking into her eyes. She looked away. "Somebody been hitting you?" he demanded.

"Like your husband, for instance," he said fiercely.

She nodded. "Yeh, he's been badly using me, as they say round here, but it's me own fault. I'm horrible to him, I just can't stand him near me."

Terry felt his gorge rising; he became white with rage.

"That doesn't give him the right to thump you,"he spat out, "ahll kill the bastard."

She stroked his cheek to calm him.

"Ahm not in a position to judge him, after all I'm cheating on him with you, and he is sorry, he's promised he'll never do it again."

"They always say that," he raged, "till the next time."

She kissed him gently on the mouth, then straddling him, offered her small breasts to be kissed. Soon they were locked in their own private world of joy, while the flames of the now blazing fire licked their way up the chimney. In the calm afterglow that followed, they lay entwined in the warm bed, troubles and anger forgotten, listening to the sound of Eccles the mouse remorselessly crunching his way through Terry's stock of coal.

Requiem for
Jackie Hogg

Eric and Terry strolled down the cobbled street of the Cloth Market one Wednesday night, indulging in a mid-week pub-crawl. Eric, having found some part-time work as a labourer, had money in his pocket and the kind of thirst that only hard manual toil can produce. They were heading for the Old George, which almost invariably contained a few of the Squatters among its clientele. They entered the old building with its stone flagstones and oak beamed ceilings, making their way to the back room, a study in wood panelling and nicotine. The Squatters were indeed there, in fact they were out in force and had been in residence for some time as evidenced by the empty brown ale bottles littering the tables, yet they seemed strangely subdued. Alex did not keep them in suspense for too long as their reason for this uncharacteristic solemnity. "Sit down, lads," he said, "his big dark eyes devoid of their usual sparkle, "ahv got some bad news. Jackie Hogg's dead, aye, 'drownded' up at Hexham, in the river."

It appeared that Jackie, having had a few lunch time beers, had made his way down to the river and in his usual gregarious fashion got into conversation with a young canoeist practising his skills in the shallows. Jackie - always an enthusiast of outdoor pursuits - persuaded the youth to let him try his hand at the paddling game and was soon midstream, heading down river at a fair pace. He rounded a bend, disappearing behind a clump of weeping willows and the young man never saw him or his canoe again. Hank took up the tale. "They didn't find him till four days later, miles downstream, he must have gone over and couldn't right his self, the stupid bastard, he'd never been in a canoe in he's life."

"Why, aye he had," chipped in Spud. "Ah remember he told me about it." A fierce argument ensued on the subject of Jackie's canoeing skills, until Red quelled them all with a bellow. "Look, it's no good arguing about it, he's gone now, and the worst thing is wi didn't find out about it till he was dead and buried."

Jackie 'Animal' Hogg's death was a tragedy among this close-knit group, made all the more poignant by the fact that his family had seen fit to go through the inquest and conduct his funeral without letting his friends know. Needless to say, that Wednesday night turned out to be one of more than average drunkenness and bad behaviour, which the landlord, in his wisdom, totally ignored, being very fond of Jackie himself. As Terry and Eric were leaving, Alex shouted after them,

"Anyway lads, it's Rothbury this weekend, wha all gannin, divvent miss it."

They decided not to miss it and that Saturday they were among the crowd of about forty or so who descended on the luckless town of Rothbury. The afternoon went quietly, with a stroll round the town taking in several of the hostelries, then Alex led the way out of town to stash their gear. He had spotted a large stack of straw bales in a field on the outskirts which commanded a good view of the surrounding countryside. They excavated the centre of the stack, lining the bales round the edge in interlocking formation to form walls, then hid their bindles in the resulting well. From the ground, the stack looked perfectly normal, with no clue as to what it contained, a regular Trojan horse on the outskirts of the little market town. When evening arrived, they headed into town to congregate at The Railway, a popular pub which was already quite full of tourists and locals. Spud decided that there was insufficient seating for him and his friends, so he decided to take steps to remedy the matter. Being a miner by profession, he had access to explosive materials, so on the pretence of poking the fire, he placed a detonator in the grate, then stepped back to await the results. Within a short time, there was a deafening explosion and the room was full of smoke and ash. "Right lads," said Spud with a satisfied grin. " Ah reckon wi can get wha selves sat down". This incident set the tone for the evening and by closing time that night they had succeeded in having themselves barred from every pub in the town. They then descended on the Saturday night dance and proceeded to fight everyone of fighting age. The battle spilled out onto the street and down to the river, resulting in a great many people becoming exceedingly wet. By the time the local police had summoned help from the nearby town of Alnwick, the Squatters had disappeared into the night and were safely hidden in their straw castle. From this vantage point, they could watch a Black Maria and a couple of police cars driving aimlessly around the country lanes in a fruitless search for the troublemakers. The next day, no pub would serve them and they had to make it to Alnwick before they could get a drink. The Alnwick pubs were full of talk of a riot in Rothbury involving hundreds of youths and by Tuesday the Newcastle Evening Chronicle sported a front-page headline, "TWENTY-FOUR HOUR TERROR HITS ROTHBURY!" Jackie Hogg had been laid to rest.

Rothbury proved to be something of a swan song for the Squatters. By the end of the year, Alex and Jean were married and many of the others had begun to settle down, or in some cases move on to even wilder times. The citizens of the market towns of rural Northumberland could look forward to peaceful times.

We've gotta get out of this place

During the next few weeks, Terry thought constantly of Hazel and how it would be if they were together, but she was married and seemed determined to make her marriage work. He continued to do the rounds with Johnny, who by now was itching to get back to playing the drums. Just to keep his hand in, Johnny began to play weekends at Windy Nook Working Mens' Club with The Norman Brown Trio. During the week he often deputised for other drummers, sitting in with Chas Chandler's band, The Kontors, and the Mike Carr Trio, or occasionally as a duo with Alan Price. Eric, too, was driven to carry on singing and would get up with the Mighty Joe Young Band, or any Trad outfit willing to give him a spot. Even though he resented Pricey for precipitating the break-up of the K.C.5. he deigned to appear with him, for a one-off gig at Baily's night club South Shields, with Johnny on drums and Chas on bass.

Things were slow on the run up to Christmas 1962, so Terry was glad when Johnny announced, that he was appearing at the Club A-Go-Go's Jazz lounge, with the Mike Carr Trio and would Terry like to give a hand carrying the drums? Once the kit was installed, they slipped down stairs and out into Percy Street to the Three Bulls Heads for a few pints of decent beer, racing back just in time for Johnny to take the stage. Terry sat near the front and marvelled at the virtuosity of the band, reflecting that they would receive much greater acclaim if they were to move to London. He was drinking steadily and was heading towards the bar for another, when he literally bumped into a slim girl with short red hair, wearing a skimpy black cocktail dress and stilletto heels. She turned to face him.

"Hello Terry" she said, "I didn't want to come cos I thought you might be here, but Barry insisted, he seems to think it's the in place."

Hazel was the last person he'd ever expect to meet in this club. Instinctively, he reached out for her. "You look beautiful" he said, but she fended him off.

"He'll be back in a minute, he's just gone to the toilet."

Terry was drunk enough not to care about her husband and Hazel seemed unconcerned, so he stayed and chatted, telling her about the club and pointing out Eric's artistic efforts. Eventually a blonde-haired young man made his way through the crowd towards them. He wore a suit and had the bloated look of someone who had partaken of too many business lunches. Hazel introduced them.

"Barry, this is Terry, I told you about him, we used to get the last bus together."

Barry was noticeably drunk and sported a belligerent expression.

"Ah yes, the fuckin Beatnik," he slurred. "What do yi think you're doing chatting up my wife?"

"Ahm not chatting her up" replied Terry levelly, "we've known each other since school days, we're just talking."

"Well, now you've finished talking, you can start walking," came the reply.

Hazel placed her hand on her husband's arm. He roughly brushed her hand away.

"Keep out of this, woman, this is between me and him."

This particular Geordie cliché would normally have made Terry smile, but the sight of this lout's treatment of Hazel turned him white with rage. He could see the podgy hands clenching into fists and knew there had to be a fight. He remembered advice from the Frankie contingent of the Squatters, - who talked of little else but fighting - to always get the first punch in and never draw your fist back as it gave a warning.

"Ah see yah pretty good at pushing wimmin around", he said, to give himself a few seconds.

He could see the podgy stomach straining against the striped shirt and before Barry could reply, he let loose a right, putting all his weight and anger behind it. He was right on target, his fist sunk into the flab and Barry exhaled mightily before doubling over at the waist clutching his stomach. Terry surprised himself by following through and kneeing him in the face as he went down. The luckless Barry lay groaning, as Terry stood over him, the adrenaline coursing through his body, experiencing mixed emotions of exultation and fear. He had just committed the cardinal sin of causing trouble in a night club and the bouncers had seen it all. Within seconds he was out of the door on to the landing, being soundly beaten by two gorillas in smart suits - tuxedos had yet to become derigueur. He tried to escape down the stairs but they chased after him and trapped him on the next landing and beat him to the ground. That was when he felt the boot go in. They kicked him until they drew blood then bundled him down the rest of the stairs into the street.

"That'll teach yi ti start trouble in wor club," came the profound comment from the more articulate of the two, as they walked away dabbing fastidiously at any real or imaginary spots of blood on their clothing. Terry stood swaying, gradually becoming aware of the copious amounts of blood pouring from a cut in his forehead. He reached into his pocket and pulled out a rather grubby, crinkly handkerchief and attempted to staunch the flow. He felt no pain and gradually the cool night air began to sober him up. He wondered how Hazel was and as he leaned back against the wall thinking of her and the times they had spent together, it slowly dawned on him that he wanted her and needed her. Perhaps this was how it felt to be in love. As he stood there running this consideration through his mind, two people emerged from the door of the club. It was interval time and band leader Mike Carr had stepped outside with his brother Ian for a breath of fresh air, or perhaps to smoke a joint. Their faces bore expressions of shock as they beheld Terry's bloody figure and they approached him with concern. "What happened?" asked Mike.

All that Terry could think of was that these were modern jazzmen, real cool dudes, so he answered them in a manner that he deemed appropriate.

"Like they kicked me, man," he mumbled.

"Too right," said Ian, "let's get you inside and cleaned up."

He was not too keen to go back in, but allowed himself to be led back up stairs where he was looked after by the very same bouncers who had inflicted the damage. They showed neither surprise nor remorse, simply took him to the office, cleaned him up, dressed the wound with lint and a huge strip of plaster and advised him to go to the hospital for a couple of stitches. He was determined to see the night out so they led him to a seat, bought him a drink and left him to it.

His first thought was for Hazel, but she and her husband had obviously left the scene. Johnny had just heard of his troubles and joined him at his table, along with Eric and a few of the others who had arrived at the interval. With all his mates around him he soon forgot his aches and pains and was soon telling the tale of his adventure, missing out the part about his feelings towards Hazel. After the gig was over, Eric and Johnny walked round to the Royal Victoria Hospital, where they joined the rest of the walking wounded waiting to be patched up. The forlorn casualties of a Friday night out in Newcastle.

The next morning Terry did not feel too bad but as the weekend progressed his condition worsened. Sunday night found him in the

Percy Arms, on Percy Street, with the rest of the crowd. By now his head was throbbing and by nine o-clock he admitted defeat and went home. When he arose on Monday morning he took one look in the cracked old mirror and realised he was not going to work. By now his face had taken on the look of a partly deflated football with the laces as his forehead. Luckily there was a doctor's surgery on West Parade and by Monday afternoon he was back in the R.V.I. with a suspected fractured skull. To his relief the tests were negative and he was soon back home in bed taking pain killers washed down with Lucozade. He lay in a dream world, drifting in and out of sleep, until the next day when he heard a tap on the door. He knew it was Hazel.

There was no point in trying to make himself presentable, so he threw on a shirt and opened the door. Just the sight of her made him feel better, but the sight of him gave her a shock which she valiantly tried to conceal. He grinned or at least he hoped it looked like a grin.

"Don't worry, it's not as bad it looks, nothing broken."

She made him get back into bed and fussed around tidying up.

"I've been to your work and George told me you were off. Oh Terry, this is all my fault."

He could see the tears welling up.

"Don't be daft," he said, "it's nobody's fault. Look, if you can stand it, ah could do with a cuddle."

She threw herself into his arms and began to sob.

"I've left him Terry, I've left the bastard. I've gone back to me Mam's."

"He hasn't been hitting you again, has he?" he demanded.

She looked up and smiled through her tears.

"No, he daren't, he thinks you're a hard case. He thinks you're going to beat him up."

Terry laughed, wincing with pain.

"Ahm no hard case, it was just a lucky punch. Ah caught him off his guard."

"Maybe you're not, but you're harder than him. He's only any good at hitting wimmin."

"Have you told him about us," he asked.

"Only about the park, he thinks you've got a girl friend. I'm not leaving him because of you, Terry. The way he was on Friday night, he's often like that when he gets drunk, either that or ah don't see him. But this time he got his come-uppance, you'll never know how much I enjoyed seeing him go down. No, we had a big argument and it turns out he's been screwing some girl from the office for months. So that's it. I've made my mind up. I'm never going back."

"What about Charlotte?" asked Terry.

"My mum and dad will look after her," Hazel replied, "she sees more of her Grandad than she does of her Dad anyway. I'll go back to work, they always said they would take me back anytime."

"Have you told them about me?" queried Terry, "do they know where you are now?"

"I've told them that you're a friend who got beaten up because of Barry causing trouble. That's true enough. Anyway they don't like him, they think he's arrogant."

Hazel continued to visit him every day, bringing and cooking food for him and cleaning up his room. By the end of the week the place was spotless and he was up and about. As he was on the sick, he did not wish to be seen around the town so he and Hazel took to visiting the Dodds Arms in the next street. The shabby little pub was pleasant enough during the day and the down-at-heel clientele seemed to accept their presence. Friday afternoon found them together in Terry's now spotless room. Hazel was ironing at his tiny kitchen table while Terry cleaned his cowboy boots. He watched her small hands with inordinate pleasure as she pressed, patted and folded, intent on her task, her lovely face relaxed and content. He stood the boots in the corner and stood beside her as she worked, his arm draped around her slim waist.

"I love you, Hazel Polwarth," he whispered, using her maiden name.

She stood the iron upright and took him in her arms.

"And I love you, Terry Molloy, I've loved you ever since you took me to that party at Chunkie Bourne's house. I think I even loved you a little bit when we used to get the last bus together, but I didn't think we suited each other. I thought we were too different."

"But we're not really, at least not anymore. Besides, if we love each other, that's all that matters."

They kissed each other, a long drawn out loving kiss.

"I want you to come and live with me," he said, "you and Charlotte. But not here, we've got to get out of this place. I've been saving up for the deposit on a house."

He looked out of the window. An old car - probably stolen - had been abandoned in the street and the local urchins were using it as a plaything. The boys were practising what would no doubt be their means of making their living when they grew up, by dismantling the car. The girls were in the back seat, where many of them would probably earn their money.

"There's a better life for you and me," he said, "and Charlotte of course."

"Poor little sods," she said.

"Yes, Terry, I'll come and live with you, I'm not going to let you go now, I'm never going to let you go."

True to her word Hazel did go back to work, so they did not see as much of each other as they would have liked. They had to consider the needs of Charlotte who was confused and upset by the changes going on in her small world. Terry saw them both at the weekends, taking them to the Tatler Cinema on Northumberland Street, which showed a programme of cartoon films running all day. Charlotte's favourite was Bugs Bunny, a preference which she shared with Terry and they amused each other with the catch phrases. "What's up Doc," or "That pesky wabbit," would always make the little girl giggle.

Christmas came and went. Cold winter nights and family commitments kept them apart, but it did not dull their ardour. Whenever possible they went looking at houses together, as Terry with the assistance of Bill Davidson was going through the process of applying for a mortgage.

Terry had not seen Johnny for some time and when they next met, his old friend was accompanied by a beautiful dark-haired girl, whom he recognised as Ann Armstrong, Johnny's erstwhile dancing partner. The two had a look of permanence about them, that might well have made Terry jealous, if it was not for his own love affair. Johnny',s other big news was that he was now a professional musician. The Norman Brown Trio had won a residency at "Emmersons", a swish night-club of the old fashioned kind, with a strict dress code and older clientele. He had given up his day job and was playing six nights a week for the awesome sum of £15 a week.

The Beatles

At the same time as things were changing in Johnny's life, something was happening in the music industry that was about to bring about the most profound changes since Elvis Presley burst onto the scene in 1956. The Beatles - whose first single "Love Me Do" was still appreciated by pop aficionados, - came into the charts at No. 1 in February 1963, with their second single "Please Please Me." This stayed near the top, until they achieved their second No. 1 with, "From Me To You" in May of that year.

Probably the most important difference between The Beatles and the pop stars that had gone before them, was the fact that they wrote their own songs. This single innovation inspired other aspiring bands to try their hands at song writing, leading to a situation where a new band would be unlikely to achieve recognition without some song writing ability.

The advent of The Beatles opened the way for other Liverpool groups, notably Gerry and The Pacemakers and Billy J. Kramer and The Dakotas, both managed by Beatles manager Brian Epstein. For the first time the focal point was moving away from London and provincial musicians were able to make their mark without moving to the capital. The Searchers, Brian Poole and The Tremeloes, Freddy and the Dreamers and the Dave Clark Five all achieved recognition that year, only the latter being London-based.

The Beatles rush-released an L.P. "Please Please Me" which again broke new ground in the pop world, as it did not contain the hit singles. Neither did the material consist of dross, thrown together to cash in on their recent success. Almost every song on the record could have been a hit in its own right, as was evinced by the fact that it topped the charts for 30 weeks. In fact, for a great many of the singles-buying teenagers of the day, it was the first time they had switched their record players from 45r.p.m.to 33r.p.m. and played an L.P. The Beatles created a new sound, which was to be copied by a great many pop groups seeking the magical formula for success.

However, for anyone scanning the gig guide of music papers such as the Melody Maker, or the New Musical Express, it was clear to see that rhythm & blues was fast becoming the alternative music on the pub and club circuit in London, with new young groups such as the Rolling Stones, The Who, and The Yardbirds - who featured Eric Clapton as lead guitarist - attracting large audiences.

Back in Newcastle, Alan Price was not blind to these developments so he and - the ever-astute - Chas Chandler teamed up with Eric to form a new band, adding Nigel Stanger on sax and Barry Preston on drums. Disregarding the more esoteric names currently fashionable among fledgling groups, they went out under the unwieldy title of the Alan Price Rhythm and Blues Combo. A choice that probably had more to do with Pricey's ego than any attempt to market the group.

The Alan Price
Rhythm & Blues Combo

Terry's attempts at house buying had finally borne fruit and he'd chosen two weeks in August, when the factory was closed for the annual holidays, to sign the papers and make the move.

Johnny was prone to spend some of his day-time leisure in the Grape Vaults, so he and Terry arranged to meet and share the exotic pleasures of drinking on a mid-week afternoon. They were on to their second pint and enjoying lunch, in the form of a Dickmans pork pie, when the door swung open to admit a shaft of sunlight, framing the broad shoulders of Chas Chandler.

He grinned hugely. "Ah thought ah might find yih here,"he said, "mind if ah join yih?"

He was soon firmly ensconced with a bottle of brown ale in front of him and a freshly lit cigarette in his hand. He poured some of the beer into a half pint glass, took an appreciative sip, then got down to business. "It's like this Johnny, yi know me and Pricey have started a new band with Eric. Well, the drummers not fitting in, di yih fancy takin his place?"

Johnny wiped the pork fat from his chin before replying.

"Sorry, Chas. Ahd love to, but ahm making £15 a week with Norman Brown, ahve got to make a living."

Chas laughed. "Well, that's no problem, wha doing really well, ah can give yih £14 just for starters."

That was it. Johnny was hooked. To be paid a living wage, for playing the music he loved was his idea of heaven. His first gig with the band was scheduled for the 11th of September, a midnight to 3a.m. spot at the Downbeat. A few celebratory pints later, the three parted company and Terry weaved his way back to East Parade for the last time.

That evening George Stoves arrived to help him move and together they filled an old tin trunk with his meagre belongings. They set off towards Westmorland Road, carrying it between them, hoping that the neighbours would not see them go.

"Ah wonder how long it'll be before they break in and do the gas meter", mused George.

"Once they know ahm gone they'll have the furniture, the gas pipes and the floor boards an all, more than likely," laughed Terry.

"Anyway, ahv told Mr Singh, he'd better get himself up here sharpish."

They carried on without looking back, and were soon on Westmorland Road heading for the Central Station. The coast train took them to West Jesmond station and from there it was but a short walk to Lonsdale Terrace and Terry's new home. So far, the only items of furniture were a double bed, a kitchen table and two chairs. Not yet a suitable abode for Hazel and Charlotte, but it was a start and at least it was a better neighbourhood. He rewarded George with a couple of pints at The Lonsdale pub, then with a fish and chip supper inside him, bedded down for the night in his new home. As he drifted off to sleep, he wondered how Eccles the mouse would manage without him.

Hazel considered it imperative for him to meet her parents, so that they could at least put a face to the name she was so often referring to. So Sunday morning found him on the No.4 bus, to have his Sunday dinner with the Polwarth family. The day went well, him being a local lad and interested in beer, pigeons and allotments seemed to satisfy her father. Her mother was pleased to see that he had good manners and was prepared to help with the washing up. The person who made him the most welcome was Charlotte. She took him by the hand and showed him her toys. He read stories to her and they played and chatted together like the good friends they had become.

Trading on their good opinion, he took a chance and asked if Hazel could accompany him to see the new band, knowing that it would mean her staying out all night. These good people seemed tuned in to their daughter's feelings and were glad to see her happy. They loved looking after Charlotte and seemed to trust Terry, so it was agreed that she could be with him on the big night. On the evening of the 25th Terry was leaning against the steamed-up window of the Haymarket café, awaiting Hazel's arrival at the adjoining bus station. He was wearing his latest acquisition, a brand new Levi jacket, one of the first available in Britain, which after suitable pummelling, washing and scrubbing had been rendered fit to wear. Under the denim jacket was a red checked shirt, his ragged patched Levi jeans fitted snugly over a pair of scuffed cowboy boots. Every so often the door of the little café swung open allowing the smell of cappuccino coffee, fried food and thin gravy to escape into the night air and mix with the acrid stench of diesel fumes.

He watched the bus draw in and disgorge its crowd of Saturday night revellers and from within their ranks stepped Hazel, quiet, serene and beautiful. She walked across the road towards him, her green eyes sparkling a greeting, a fitted black coat clinging to her slim form, her feet encased in black high heels which clicked their way through the rainbowed puddles as she approached.

They clung together, then walked off arm in arm down Northumberland Street, lost to the hubbub of the other young couples passing by. For the first time they were out together as a couple without the nagging fear of being seen. They were heading for the Duke of Wellington, a tiny pub in Carliol Square, near to the Downbeat.

When they arrived the small lounge was packed, but they managed to get round a table with Johnny, Ann, Eric, and Doreen. Terry proudly introduced Hazel to his friends, a moment fraught with uncertainty for them both, but they need not have worried. Ann too was a new girl and the ebullient Doreen soon put them at their ease. Terry looked round the room. Most of the Simpson's crowd were there along with some of the Squatters. Just at that moment Chas Chandler made his entrance, along with Alan Price and someone Terry recognised as Hilton Valentine, lead guitarist with The Wildcats. After getting the drinks in, Chas came over to their table and introduced Hilton to Johnny.

"This is the new guitarist ah was telling yih about, he's been playing with wih since Nigel left. Ah know yih haven't rehearsed with him but ahm sure you'll manage."

Johnny shook the proffered hand and laughed. "Aye, ahm sure whi will, after all it's only rock and roll."

They did a great deal

The beginnings of prosperity
Eric at the A-Go-Go sporting a new leather jacket

more than manage. When they took to the stage at midnight and looked out onto a capacity crowd of expectant young people, they were inspired The first number was the Screaming Jay Hawkins song "I Put A Spell On You" which proved to be a prophetic choice. The audience were spellbound from the outset, the band could do no wrong. They were a revelation to Terry. Since he last heard them, Pricey had bought himself an electric piano, a Vox Continental, which filled out the sound and complemented Hilton's lead guitar. For once, Johnny had a good solid bass line from Chas to drive the band along leaving him free to weave elaborate patterns of rhythm on his now more extensive drum kit. Eric was in fine form, his voice ranging from a deep throaty growl to a high pitched scream, he worked the crowd into a sweaty frenzy.

For the first time Terry took to the dance floor with Hazel, not quite sure what to expect, but he need not have worried. She was a precise and fluid dancer and once they had adapted to each other's style, they, as in the lyrics of so many songs, danced the night away. Indeed the night did fly past and after the band had played the last of its many encores, it was three in the morning.

Hazel was fascinated to see that many of the audience had brought sleeping bags and were bedding down for the night, but she did not have much time to observe the phenomenon. Terry knew that a milk train heading for the coast would soon be passing through nearby Manors Station. They hurried across Carliol Square and made the station with minutes to spare. The old train, with a string of freight cars and one passenger carriage, wheezed to a stop for two or three minutes then pulled out again with the two lovers on board.

They had their choice of seats in the near empty carriage and the sleepy pair clung together as the train picked up speed. West Jesmond soon hove into view and Terry congratulated himself on having found a house near the station. Five minutes later he was carrying Hazel over the threshold of what he hoped would soon be her new home. The place was overpoweringly silent after the noise of the club. They took off their shoes and spoke in whispers as Terry lit the gas fire and put the kettle on the stove for tea. They sat on the kitchen chairs and talked of the night's events, the sound of the music still ringing in their ears.

Leaving the gas fire on, they prepared themselves for bed, draping their clothes over the chairs to keep them from the dusty floor. Terry had a few white candles dotted around the place in an attempt to provide a bit of atmosphere, and he watched with reverential awe as she padded naked round the room lighting each one, the light of the flames dancing on her perfect body. She blew out the final match and he could smell the sulphur in the air as she stood before him, her bewitching green eyes looking deeply into his. He took her to him and they made love gently and slowly, never wanting it to end and trusting each other that it never would.

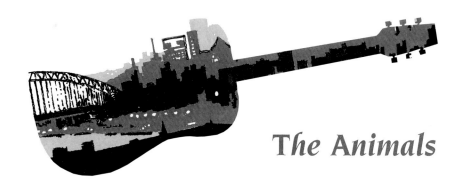

The Animals

The inception of the Alan Price Rhythm and Blues Combo, coincided almost exactly with the explosion of The Beatles and it could not be denied that the fame of the latter, contributed to the popularity of the former, as young people turned away from the established formulaic pop stars and looked for something new and exciting. By the end of December 1963 The Beatles had five singles in the top twenty, including two extended players. The Newcastle band were working five nights a week, enjoying relative fame after so many years in the wilderness.

Bill Davidson continued to have weekend parties and the band were often present. In their search for new material, they pillaged Bill's record collection, turning again and again to Bob Dylan. Eventually it was decided that "Baby Let Me Follow You Down" might stand the rhythm and blues treatment. This was a song that Dylan attributed to a young blues singer from Boston by the name of Ric Von Schmidt who probably would not have relished the band's bowdlerised version, with the lyrics changed to "Baby Let Me Walk You Home". The other song which took their fancy was "The House Of The Rising Sun", a rendition of which some of them already knew from a recording by Leadbelly. Hilton took Dylan's guitar lick as a basis for his own introduction to the song and for his part, Dylan had been inspired by folk singer Dave Van Ronk's arrangement of this traditional lament of a New Orleans' woman, driven into prostitution by poverty.

By the beginning of 1964 more new British bands were making it into the charts, with the Swinging Blue Jeans, the MerseyBeats and the Hollies all making the top ten. The only rhythm and blues band to achieve chart success was Manfred Mann, who only made it by recording 5-4-3-2-1, a song in no way representative of their stage act. The London R&B groups were beginning to get gigs in the provinces and Mike Jeffries, ever on the look out for something new, began to book them for the A-Go-Go, notably The Yardbirds - who had replaced Eric Clapton with Jeff Beck - and the Graham Bond Organisation, a blues group with Jack Bruce on bass and Ginger Baker on drums: Bond himself being one of the many musicians to have passed through Blues Incorporated. Bond was very impressed by the Newcastle band, as was Georgio Gomelky, manager of The Yardbirds. So much so, that Mike Jeffries began to consider that it was about time they got themselves a manager. Inspired perhaps by the success of Brian Epstein, he put himself up for the job and soon had a contract drawn up for them to sign. Like so many young groups before them, they signed with enthusiasm and without reading the small print. Perhaps, suffice to say, they lived to regret their haste.

Jeffries was soon off to London at the invitation of Gomelsky who introduced him to Ronan O'Reilly, the owner of the Scene Club. This club featured all the currently popular R&B groups and had connections with other clubs such as the Ricky Tick and the Crawdaddy. A deal was struck. O'Reilly and Gomelsky would organise work for Jeffries' group if he would promote the London groups in the North East. There was one stipulation: the band would have to dispense with the lugubrious title of the Alan Price Rhythm and Blues Combo and opt for something snappier. The ideal place for the discussion of such a topic was a pub, and the one the band used when playing the A-Go-Go was the Three Bulls Heads on Percy Street. They were gathered there one night with a few of the rest of the crowd for a pre-gig beverage when they were joined by their new manager with his proposal for a name change.

Everyone apart from Pricey, thought it was a good idea and new names began to be bandied about.

"Whiv got The Beatles, what about The Rats?" suggested Chas.

"Or The Crows", said Hilton.

Everyone began to chip in and once they had run out of all the beasts of the fields and the birds of the air, they began on inanimate objects, like cars and motor-bikes. Then on to architectural features such as The Quaysiders, or The Greys Monuments. Now they were hitting their stride in the absurdity stakes. The Bigg Markets was suggested, The St. James's Parks and The Tyne Bridges. When they started on the city's pubs, Jeffries, never noted for his sense of humour, began to lose patience. Then Eric stepped in with a suggestion.

"Why not name us after Jackie Hogg, what about Animal Hogg and The Squatters."

Pricey, by now resigned to the change, spoke up for the first time.

"That's too long, but what about The Animals, wouldn't that be suitable?"

Pints were lifted, cigarettes were lit, or extinguished and chairs were shuffled. Somehow this one had struck a chord. Finally Johnny spoke up.

"Ah reckon that'll do it, anyone else agree?"

Eric, Chas and Hilton gave the nod, and so it was agreed, The biggest group ever to come out of the North East were to be called The Animals.

It was Saturday July 5th 1964, the morning sun was warming the fronts of the houses on Lonsdale Terrace. The door of No. 13 opened and out stepped Terry Molloy, wearing faded Levi jeans cowboy boots and a black tee shirt. He turned and took the hand of a little girl of about three years old. She was wearing pink dungarees and a pink striped tee shirt. Her long red hair was a tumbling mass of curls tied up with a green ribbon, she hugged a plastic bag to her chest. Behind her was Hazel Polwarth, with short hair, the same startling colour as the child's. She wore a very short red dress buttoned down the front, her long slim legs were bare and her small feet were just held in skimpy sandals.

Terry relieved Charlotte of her burden, which contained bread to feed the ducks and she walked between them, reaching up to hold their hands and asking to be swung every few steps. So they made their way down Lindisfarne Road towards Jesmond Dene. Charlotte's father Barry was supposed to have her on Saturdays, but he came less and less and she had learned not to rely on him.

As was his custom Terry bought the Melody Maker plus some sweets for the child. He thrust the paper into the bag with the bread and they carried on, the sun growing warmer as it reached its zenith in the cloudless sky. When they reached the Dene, they were glad of its leafy shade as they walked down towards the stream that had spent so many years carving out this deep cleft in the soft rock. They chose a seat near the water in the dappled shade and Terry retrieved his paper from the bag which Charlotte carried off to the waters edge. With total concentration she took a handful of bread and used her whole body to cast it into the waters, laughing with delight when the ducks, already congregating there, began to squabble over every morsel.

Terry opened his paper. The whole of the front page was taken up with a photograph of Johnny, Eric, Pricey, Chas and Hilton taken on the flat roof of a very tall building. The first thing that struck him was that it was sunny there too. The headline proclaimed , "Animals straight in at No. 1." He sat stunned for a moment, then turned and put his arm round Hazel , showing her the paper.

"You'll never believe this, the lads have got a hit record, top of the charts, straight in at number one, they've made it."

She took the paper from him and studied the photograph.

"God its hard to believe, your mates, on the front page of The Melody Maker."

"They're your mates as well," he said.

She put her arms around his neck and kissed him.

"You won't be jealous will you Terry?" she asked anxiously, "It won't make you restless?"

He laughed, "No ahll be happy just ti bask in their reflected glory, besides, who knows how long it's going to last?"

He took the paper over to the little girl.

"Look Charlotte, your uncle Johnny and uncle Eric have got their picture in the paper, they've made a record and it's going to be played on the radio lots and lots of times, they're going to be famous and travel all over the world."

He picked her up and whirled her round.

"But we'll still be here when they get back, me, you and your mum, we're going to be great together."

She picked up on his excitement and as he whirled her in a giddy circle, the clear peels of her laughter echoed round the craggy walls of Jesmond Dene.